MW00338876

Country
Properties

Hoff's Twelve Rules for Success

1. Buy only farms and ranches that have good soils with adequate water resources.

2. Buy only farms and ranches that can make money, either from operations or from capital gains on the sale of the property. Or both!

3. Develop a business plan and a cash budget.

4. Finance only what you can afford to service.

5. Hire an honest and capable manager.

6. Select a good and honest mentor.

7. Buy only the best breeding cattle.

8. Engage a knowledgeable large-animal veterinarian.

9. Create a health program for the herd—then follow it!

10. Devise a forage-crop program, including weed control and fertilization.

11. Develop a marketing scheme for your beef cattle that is tied into your business plan.

12. Maintain your farm or ranch with great eye-appeal.

Country Properties

John K. Hoff
Jennifer L. Hoff

How to select, invest and manage land,
beef cattle and pecans

The Seville Group

Manufactured in the United States of America
ISBN: 0-9664193-0-8
Cover design: Pearl and Associates
Book design and production: Tabby House

Disclaimer

The purpose of this book is to provide information relevant to rural real estate, beef cattle and pecans. The authors and The Seville Group have used their best efforts in preparing this book and make no representations or warranties with respect to its accuracy or completeness. In addition, they specifically disclaim any implied warranties of merchantability or fitness for a particular purpose. Nor may warranties be created or extended by sales representatives or written sales material. The data and opinions stated herein are not guaranteed or warranted to produce any particular results and may not be suitable for every person. You are strongly urged to research and read all available material and tailor the information to your individual situation. The authors and publisher shall not be liable for any loss of profit or any other commercial damages, including but not limited to special, incidental, consequential or other damages. If you do not want to be bound by the contents of this disclaimer, you may return this book to the publisher for a full refund.

Publishers Cataloging in Publication
(Provided by Quality Books, Inc.)

Hoff, John K.
      Country Properties / John K. Hoff, Jennifer L.
   Hoff. -- 1st ed
      p. cm.
      Includes biographical references and index.
      Preassigned LCCCN: 98-91038
      ISBN: 0-96664193-0-8
      1. Beef cattle. 2. Ranching--United States.
   I. Hoff, Jennifer L. II. Title.
SF207.H64 1999   636.2'32
                    QBI98-1760

The Seville Group
17 Briar Hollow, Ste. 205
Houston, TX 77027-2896

Dedication

In honor of Professor John I. Miller, who was, to
my dad, a cherished friend and father-in-law, and
to me, a loving and admired granddad.

Jennifer L. Hoff

Professor John I. Miller
1911–1980

John I. Miller was born and reared in Kansas and attended Kansas
State University, obtaining the B.S. degree with honors in 1933.
After graduate studies at Cornell University, where he earned his
M.S. and Ph.D. degrees, he was invited to join the faculty, attaining
full professorship in 1944. Animal science was his profession; beef
cattle and their nutrition were his specialty. He was in charge of
beef cattle teaching and research during his tenure and was a past
president of the American Society of Animal Science. He was in-
strumental in establishing the New York Beef Cattlemen's Association, Empire Livestock Marketing Cooperative and the Beef
Cattleman's Short Course. For thirty-one years he served as secre-
tary of the New York Angus Association. Professor Miller developed the first type classification system for beef cattle. The national type classification program adopted by the American Angus
Association was based on his New York plan.

Teaching was Professor Miller's prime interest at Cornell and his
dedication to this goal was well acknowledged by his students.
They respected his mastery of the subject matter, his ability to
convey it to the students, and his fine example of personal conduct. At various times he taught five different courses annually,
taught more than 6,000 undergraduates, while also directing graduate
programs for fifty Ph.D. and twenty-five M.S. candidates. His livestock judging teams had distinguished records in national compe-

tition for more than twenty-five years. To the many farm and ranch employees and owners who depended upon him for sound, practical and professional advice, he was known to have impartiality with respect to the size of their pockets. In honor of his contributions to livestock production, especially beef cattle, he was awarded

Courtesy and permission of the Division of Rare & Manuscript Collections, Cornell University.

Professor Miller with herdsman, Ken Tillapaugh, showing the prize Angus heifer that was presented to President Dwight D. Eisenhower.

the prestigious New York Farmers' Award. His major investigations on utilization of pastures and other forages earned him wide recognition among cattlemen and animal scientists. Other significant research involved the use of pelleted forages in fattening rations, the preservation of high moisture grain with propionic acid, the study of critical protein requirements for cattle and the analysis of the quality of the beef carcass from livestock on intensive grass-fed programs. In recognition of his lifetime achievements in research he received the Distinguished Service Award from the North Atlantic Section of the American Society of Animal Science, was made an Honorary Fellow of the American Society of Animal Science and was selected for inclusion in *Who's Who in America*.

Acknowledgments

We are indebted for the assistance given to us through the years on this vast subject by many distinguished individuals. Some were professors, researchers and chief executives, but many were also "just plain" ranchers and lovers of the land, so to speak, who through their own special intellect, ingenuity and hard work, succeeded where others failed or lost interest. We all have a special debt to them.

Gratitude is also due the many people who helped this book come to fruition. Foremost must be Myron Fuerst, who not only kept us on the straight and narrow and critiqued the manuscript, but also provided a reservoir of encouragement and enthusiam. Many thanks also to Dan Sisler, Professor Emeritus of Agricultural Economics, Cornell University, and to George Conneman, Professor of Agricultural, Resource and Management Economics, Cornell University, for their review and helpful comments; to Graham Williams, President, International Partners, for critiquing the manuscript as well as for his wisdom and support; and to Greg Miller for reminding us the ABC's of grammer and punctuation.

Praise and gratitude must also be expressed to others who contributed to getting the manuscript into a commercial book such as Galen Struve, whose line drawings and color painting added so much to the presentation and educational value of the work.

Finally, we also would like to thank Professor John I. Miller for instilling a love of the land and the beef cattle industry in his family.

Quick Check

Part One—Getting Started

Part Two—Operating the Ranch

Part Three—Exotic Diversions

Part Four—Winding Down

Appendices

Preface

This book is an outgrowth of an obvious demand from potential farm and ranch buyers who needed a clearer picture of what they were getting into—the authors discovered this during their many years marketing agricultural properties. While most potential buyers were sophisticated in the business world, they were almost completely ignorant about how to become a successful rancher. The most astounding thing about this mentality was their overconfidence in thinking that they knew what they were doing despite their lack of relevant knowledge. Many affluent buyers are highly educated, often in technology or the law, and they have strong opinions. Unfortunately, when it comes to ranching, their opinions are usually not based on essential facts or thoughtful evaluations. It is interesting to reflect on how these otherwise astute and clearly successful individuals would react if they had a serious medical ailment or a potentially catastrophic business problem. They would seek out the best surgeon or medical specialist in the country or experienced business professional.

But with rural real estate and the ranching business, almost every novice sees themselves as experts. They have ideas and hunches from friends, commercial brokers, or whomever. There is no shortage of unqualified advice or misinformation. In fact, many spend upwards of $10–12 million for a ranch based on such prejudicial nonsense, then face the pain of reality.

We hope this book, in the form of a practical management guide to evaluating and managing ranch property, will help solve these problems. This book is not the last word on the many technical subjects related to agriculture or real estate, but rather is a straightforward, logical sequential summation of these subjects as they relate to the ranching industry. We have studied the latest published data and added, from years of actual experience, our thoughts and the views of others in the ranching business, to synthesize an integrated overview for anyone contemplating the purchase of a ranch. It should provide guidance to potential owners so that they have a basis for evaluation and management founded on facts, not from fragments of information from amateurs in the field. We have included references from a wide spectrum of time; from the latter part of the nineteenth century, when the Department of Agriculture, the Homestead Act, and the Land-Grant Act were born, to others from current publications. You are encouraged to refer to and read some of these references to develop a better understanding of how far we have come in this industry.

The beef we eat now is approximately fifteen months of age, instead of three to four years as it was in the beginning of this century. Appreciate how this acceleration in growth is the result of the improvement in feed quality from better forages, and the introduction of protein supplements, vitamins and improved genetics. From a financial standpoint, appreciate how this helps the rate of return on your investment and enables the American beef industry to be so competitive and the envy of the world.

It is also interesting to note how infinitely complex most of the subject matter is, but how very simple the principles are, e.g., biochemical pathways versus the principle to provide higher quality and more nutritious feed, or embryo transplantation versus improved cow efficiency. The principles were essentially the same at the beginning of the century as they are today, but the techniques have become more sophisticated.

Professionals in the real estate and ranching industries may find the condensed overview of such a large subject helpful. With this in mind, we include an extensive table of contents which we call *Quick Check*.

This book is not only a collaboration between father and daughter, as exciting and perilous as that may be, but also the ideas, opinions and research of others, some not here on earth now, but never far when we think about land, beef cattle and pecans. We hope you will be wiser and wealthier from not only reading *Country Properties*, but by using it in the pursuit of your dream.

Historical Setting

When Horace Greeley, the crusading founder, owner and editor of the old *New York Tribune*, coined the phrase in the mid-nineteenth century, "Go west, young man," he didn't know the magnitude nor the implications of his seemingly innocuous suggestion. Or was it a prophecy? Whichever it was, the results are in. New York is no longer the most populous state in the Union. We are as far west as one can go in these continental United States, with a few cities, such as Chicago, Kansas City, Houston, Dallas, San Antonio, Denver, Phoenix, thrown in along the way!

What the western movement found was thousands upon thousands of Texas Longhorn cattle wandering freely on the range. It is estimated that 10 million head of Texas cattle with a market value in excess of $200 million were driven to northern markets in the latter part of the nineteenth century. Mr. Greeley's newspaper, circulated in England, Scotland and parts of Europe, ignited the interests and passions of wealthy types on the other side of the Atlantic and it was not long before Scottish and English money found its way into the American West via investments in large ranching and beef cattle operations. In fact, the basis for today's ranch and cattle business is the importation of British breeds of cattle in the early years of ranch formation and evolution.

Imported breeds such as Shorthorn, Hereford, and Angus had a major influence in the cattle industry and ranching culture. While much is read about the King Ranch in South Texas, actually the largest ranches in American history were the XIT ranch, which at one time included 3,500,000 deeded acres, and the Matador ranch, which at its height controlled about 2,000,000 acres, of which half was deeded. Both were in Texas but were financed and controlled by Scottish and English money, figures such as the Earl of Aberdeen and the Marquis of Tweeddale, and financiers from Dundee, Scotland. In fact, Murdo Mackenzie, a Scot who came over to the states to manage the Matador, was largely responsible for the rapid expansion of the Hereford breed in the West. He believed in both pedigree and conformation and knew the benefits of promotion. The ranch earned wide acclaim under his management and American cattlemen considered him a true Westerner.

As British livestock and money poured into the American beef industry, the next era was characterized by the amalgamation of the imported breeds into our domestic cattle, followed by the rapid expansion westward throughout our heartland. The famous ranches and their principle sires still bring pride and joy to all who read their illustrious history. There was the T.L. Miller herd in Illinois with its Hereford cattle; the C.M. Culbertson herd, with its imported bull, Anxiety 2238; the Banning-Lewis Ranch in Colorado, with Prince Domino 101 and Gudgell and Simpson with Anxiety 4th and Prince Domino. We cannot discuss Hereford cattle without mentioning the name of family friend and former Cornell University Trustee Albert K. Mitchell from New Mexico. He was twice president of the American Hereford Association and a member of the syndicate which eventually liquidated the Matador Ranch. A true gentleman, he personified the sophisticated management of large ranching operations and their accompanying beef herds in the West.

When one remembers the Polled Hereford, per se, and forgets the argumentative times of the horn/no horn registry question,

Warren Gammon and his bull, Giant, come to mind as does John M. Lewis, and his brother of Alfalfa Lawn Farm in Kansas, whom we remember showing cattle to advantage in one of the major livestock shows. While we have no true experience with the Shorthorn breed, the name E.S. Kelly and his famous two sires Whitehall Sultan and Avondale will ring a bell with Shorthorn enthusiasts.

With Zebu or Brahman blood cattle, certainly the King Ranch is the most famous, with its Brahman/Shorthorn crosses which ultimately led to the new breed, Santa Gertrudis. However, the foundation for the breed was the sire, Monkey, and for several decades more famous than the human family that developed the ranch. John K. Hoff was fortunate to be trustee for a King Ranch family member for several years and can attest to the tradition and sense of history at the old main ranch. You almost can sense that "Bob" Kleberg Jr. is lurking and ready to assume a leadership role again after bringing the ranch into such prominence almost eighty years ago. Later we will mention the value of a true confidant or mentor in the ranching business and this ranch has had one for two generations, Leroy Denman Sr. and Leroy Denman Jr. Their advice and counsel was, we believe, the major reason the ranch exists today as an entity. It truly is an American institution and we hope the family hangs in there against all odds to otherwise do so.

More recently with Brahman cattle, the J.D. Hudgins and V8 ranch herds, both in Hungerford, Texas, stand out in our minds, with both males and females of super conformation and mild dispositions. The Brangus cattle belonging to Dr. and Mrs. Herman Gardner's Willow Spring Ranch in Texas, and R.O. Anderson's Diamond A Cattle Co. in Roswell, New Mexico, reflect their owners' enthusiasm and class.

And, of course, we cannot forget the Angus breed, one of the truly remarkable beef breeds that not only has stood the test of time but has changed with the times. Early on it was the McHenry herd in Iowa, followed by Sunbeam Farms in Oklahoma with its top sire, Black Prince of Sunbeam. Later, there was the Rosemere herd from Iowa and California, which also had an early influence in the breed, not only with their bulls, Glenfoil Thickset 2nd and Oakville Quiet Lad, but through their female family. And last, but certainly not least, are Ankony Farms, first established in New York and later expanded to Nebraska and South Dakota, and the Leachman family, along with family friend, and fellow Cornellian Myron Fuerst, whom we believe to be one of the most astute cattle/businessmen in the country.

We could go on and on but you get the picture. The West was won, not by gunslingers but by dedicated missionaries—ones who used their brains and risked their money for something we call ranching. Today it is not British pounds that are financing a return to the call, "Go West, young man," but American wealth such as that of the Rockefeller family, and more recently, the Cox family of newspaper and communication fame, and Henry Singleton, co-founder of Teledyne, who has bought large operating ranch tracts.

As reported in recent issues of the *Wall Street Journal* and *Worth* magazine, Ted Turner, guru of modern-day broadcasting and his actress wife, Jane Fonda, own a total of 1.3 million acres of ranch land. Other reported newcomers to ranching have included film stars Robert Redford and Harrison Ford; former chairman of Goldman Sachs, Stephen Friedman; chairman of Louis Dreyfus et Cie of Paris and New York Gerard "William" Louis-Dreyfus; chairman of U.S. Surgical, Leon Hirsch; World Bank President, Jim Wolfensohn; clothing designer, Ralph Lauren; brokerage house entrepreneur, Charles Schwab; television journalists Sam Donaldson and Tom Brokaw; financiers, Henry Kravis, Felix Rohatyn and Herb Allen, and literally thousands of others smitten with the mystique of ranch life.

Ranching must be contagious because in June 1996, the *Houston Chronicle*, via the *L.A. Times*, had a headline story, "Rural Population on Increase." The article reported that rural regions of the United States gained 2.6 million residents from April 1990 to July 1995. Demographers who conducted the study said, "that a long-term trend toward rural growth has taken hold." This is further evidence of the current interest in rural America. It also is interesting to note that net farm and ranch income has now passed the $50 billion mark in 1996, while farm and ranch assets are believed to exceed one trillion U.S. dollars. A remarkable result in any interpretation.

What is a ranch? Historically, a ranch was generally distinguished from a farm by the fact that its main source of income was from the sale of livestock and that the source of feed was forage plants. In today's usage, we probably mean a property in the West or South capable of supporting livestock, most notably beef cattle, and ranging in size from twenty to one hundred acres for a junior weekend cowboy to large spreads where commercial livestock production is the intended goal. Unless the owner inherited the ranch there is also one other common thread that bonds the current owners— relatively large sums of cash and income from other sources. From an operational view one would be fortunate to earn, strictly from ranching activities, two percent to five percent per year on invested capital. This coupled with the wildly fluctuating prices of cattle and the many hazards of weather, disease, and possibly poor management or bad luck should quickly dispel the idea of a get-rich-quick scheme.

But why the dramatic increase in interest to own a ranch? Is it the hope for oil and gas discoveries or the development of real estate?

Usually not. Many purchasers just enjoy the pleasures of owning land and becoming an instant cowboy. For others, it is replacing a play toy, such as a yacht, which just depreciates, as opposed to productive ranchland which might be sold for profit, if one tires of the "toy." For still others, it might be the opportunity to participate in a time-honored and respected culture or it may be this tremendous mystique of being a ranch owner. A ranch is truly defined through the eyes of the beholder.

Part One:

Getting Started

Chapter 1

Ranch Acquisition

This chapter discusses the many criteria you need to evaluate while choosing the right piece of property. In the normal course of evaluation, many personal and sentimental reasons overwhelm the selection process. While being close to friends or falling in love in the back forty have their honored place in the process, other technical factors will have a greater bearing on the success of the operation, and ultimately your happiness with the decision. Here are some important issues to consider:

Selection Criteria

Location: You probably have heard the old saying in real estate circles that the three most important factors in property selection are "location, location and location." Ultimately this so-called theorem will be correct for your ranch selection, too. Many factors will characterize your location. In addition to these, proximity to friends, convenience to your main home or office, ambiance of the area, and other personal considerations will and should play a role in selecting your dream ranch.

We had a personal experience which illustrates this point. Some years back we were looking for a weekend ranch that was large enough to support a full-time employee. We looked northwest of Houston, Texas, where many of our friends had ranches, both the weekend variety and large working ones. The ambiance of the area was supreme as the view north focused on a large lake and the many storm fronts that come from the northwest. The setting gave a unique feeling to the area—especially to people from Houston, which is flat and humid. Professor John I. Miller of Cornell University, was with us. When he saw what we were contemplating buying, he almost had a coronary. His vast experience in the beef cattle industry led him to direct his attention to the productive capacity of the soils—which consisted primarily of rocks. He estimated it would take a minimum of twenty acres per cow/calf unit at a price of $2,200 per acre. Therefore, this hill of rocks would have cost $44,000 per animal unit. Hardly an economic one! While we debated the issues that day, another buyer bought the property. Of course Professor Miller thought we were saved, but we weren't completely convinced. I know he was right technically, but emotionally we were disappointed. That same property has since sold again, for ranch use, this time for almost $5,000 per acre. In reflection maybe we were both right, depending on the criteria for success.

Soils: No single factor is more important in selecting a ranch property than the soils. While there are some exceptions, as mentioned above, through the years we have become true believers in this philosophy. The soil has a major influence on the type of forage or crop that can be grown, the productivity, the ease of use, the water-holding capacity, the internal drainage, whether the foundation of your improvements will be stable, and whether septic tank fields are satisfactory. The soil imposes limitations on your ranch development and production program. The basic importance and relatively inflexibility of soil make it vital to that selection process. Careful scrutiny must be given to soil analysis and evaluation as it is extremely difficult, if not impossible, to change the soil. The rewards of a wise selection will "come home to roost" many times during your ownership of the ranch. Generally, farms and ranches can be no better than the soils that support them.

Historically, ranches were thought of as areas where the soils and terrain were poor and not suitable for crops. They were thought of as a practical use of natural resources. However, many of the ranches in the West that were operating under such soil conditions usually required a minimum of sixty acres per cow/calf unit. Hardly a phenomenon that would exist relatively close to a city where most of the weekend cowboy market thrives. In addition, today the beef business has spread from throughout the West and Midwest to the South, and it has acquired a more intensified management style. These significant developments have changed the demographics of the beef cattle entrepreneur and the weekend cowboy.

The soil is composed of broken and weathered minerals and decaying organic matter. Minerals contribute by far the greatest weight of the soil. Organic matter comprises only about ten percent or less, except in peat or muck soils. However, the organic portion is vital because of its favorable influence on the water holding capacity, friability, and nutrients, especially nitrogen. The soil is analyzed and classified by its physical characteristics and chemical properties. With minor exceptions, the former determines soil type, (such as sandy loam) and internal drainage, while the latter determines pH and available nutrients or the fertility of the soil.

Without trying to make you a soil scientist, we will attempt to explain the difference in soil properties that affect your intended land use. This should make it easier for you to understand your county's soil survey as published by the Natural Resource Conservation Service (formerly Soil Conservation Service) and your State Agricultural Extension Service. Try to obtain a copy and refer to it in your selection process.

Soil is classified one way by the physical size of the soil particle. At one end of the spectrum are the large particles, which give rise to sandy soil; on the other end one finds fine particles, giving rise to clay and clayey types. In between are the average-sized particles, and mixtures that are classified as loam, sandy loam, and clayey loam. These are usually our best agricultural soils. With large particles, along with their large interparticle space, or pores, water permeates the soil too quickly, thus having little moisture-retaining properties. At the other end of the spectrum, the finer (silts or clayey types) have little interparticle space—thus moisture doesn't move down through the strata fast enough causing the small interparticle spaces to become filled with water for long periods of time. This latter phenomenon is very serious, not only because of drainage, per se, but because the interparticle spaces of the soil will not have sufficient gaseous oxygen in the root zone, which is essential for most plant growth. In addition, fine soils are extremely difficult to work or traverse by foot, hoof, or motor vehicle. You only need to go to a wet bottomland and walk a foot or two—what a mess! An old adage here: "If you stick to the soil when its dry, it will stick to you when it's wet."

Another property of soils is its so-called soil profile or vertical horizons, e.g., topsoil, horizon A, subsoil, etc. Suffice it to say that a good deep topsoil is generally necessary for plant growth, but consideration must be made for possible "hardpans" or other impediments to root growth, plus the natural drainage of water from the soil and subsoil.

With respect to natural drainage, the USDA classifies all soils into seven categories, from excessively drained, somewhat excessively drained, well drained, moderately well drained, somewhat poorly drained, poorly drained to very poorly drained. The superb soils fall into the middle categories.

Permeability on the other hand defines the quality of the soil that enables water to move downward through the profile. It is measured as the number of inches per hour that water moves downward through a saturated soil. The USDA classification for permeability is shown in figure 1. Again, the better soils fall in the middle of the classification.

The natural fertility of the soil can be easily determined by chemical soil analysis. These procedures are usually done, and are often free, by your State Agricultural Extension Service or your local fertilizer distributor.

Category	Inches/hour
Very slow	<0.06
Slow	0.06 to 00.2
Moderately slow	0.20 to 00.6
Moderate	0.60 to 02.0
Moderately rapid	2.00 to 06.0
Rapid	6.00 to 20.0
Very rapid	> 20.0

Fig. 1. Permeability rates for soils

An excellent way to determine carrying capacity and the fertility of the soil is to observe the type and vigor of crop growth. Another way is to examine crop production records. If there are no crops to examine and if production records are lacking, the next best thing to look at is the character of vegetation present. Beech, sugar maple, pecan, hickory, black walnut and white oak trees of large size and vigor indicate good soils while white pine, cedar, scrub oak and scrawny trees of most species are typical of poor soils. Vigorous willows, poplars, cottonwood, and elder bushes may suggest too much water. Weeds also tell a tale. If the nature of the growth is lush and vigorous with very dark green leaves the expectation is that the land is satisfactory.

Topography: This site characteristic, which represents the surface features of the land, influences erosion, surface water drainage and what type of crop may be suitable for the property. For example, because of soil erosion on inclined slopes, only full-time grass may be grown as opposed to small grains and some forage crops. And even then, the cost of production may increase so that it becomes excessive. Another major consideration is how the topography influences the surface drainage. In most soils where the land is sloping or rather impervious to water a considerable amount of rain water is lost. This can cause serious erosion and flooding on the ranch property. Therefore, check on this with the local Natural Resource Conservation Service or your county agricultural agent. Many of the county road and bridge departments may also be helpful as they normally track flooding in their county. If you go to their office with a smile, you may obtain an updated one hundred-year flood plain map for your location.

You should get a topographic contour map from your local Natural Resource Conservation Service for the area you are considering. Topographic maps show various geographic features including contours, streams, and roads.

Abbreviated rules for reading a topographic map: Closeness of contour lines indicates severity of slope. Numbers in line are elevations. Thus, widely separated contours mean relatively flat land while more closely arranged contour lines signify a steeper slope. It will be essentially self-explanatory, but in case it isn't, the following map may help:

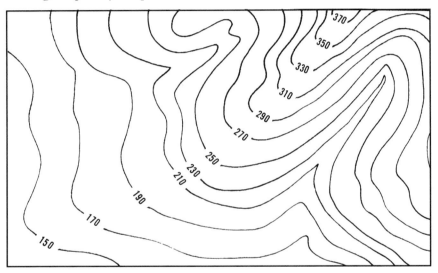

Fig.2. A hypothetical topographic map showing contour lines.

Water Supply: The importance of a large reliable supply of water for the ranch cannot be overemphasized. The amount of water required for beef cattle, exclusive of the amount contained in their feed, varies with the character of the ration, the amount of dry matter consumed, the ambient air temperature, and the size of the animal. In the Southwest, during summer this daily requirement may reach twenty to twenty-five gallons per mature 1,200 pound cow. Naturally, the streams, creeks, springs and river frontages all contribute to a low-cost water supply, but make sure the source or supply runs all year and is reliable. Distribution of rainfall also must be kept in mind. You are likely to have heavy spring rains and little or no rain in July or August. Thus, seasonal distribution must be factored into your thinking and operational program. It is highly recommended that additional sources of water be available such as water wells, which may be pumped by windmill, gas or electric pumps, or solar panels. A word of caution—if using an electrical system, ensure that the system and all metal housing for the components are well-grounded—no exceptions!

It is generally recommended that cattle should not have to walk more than one-and-a-half to two miles to find fresh water. Another aspect of the water requirement is that it be of good quality. Water containing large amounts of detrimental salts is not highly palatable to livestock or man and may cause physiological problems in both. Furthermore, the water supply needs to be clean and safe. Some ranch wells are shallow and the ground water may be contaminated. Therefore, it is a good idea to have the water supply checked to see if it meets the county health department standards. Also investigate the depth of the water table year-round to determine the rate it may drop during active pumping. It is also important to investigate the historic static level because the depth of water in the aquifer may be receding. Finally, make sure your septic tank and its field do not contaminate your potable water supply.

With respect to the homestead, research has shown that you need an average of fifty to one hundred eighty gallons per day per person for an adequate water supply. You also must estimate your peak water demand times and make sure that there is sufficient capacity available from your well and pumping/delivery system. Always plan on the high side of your estimates. Another good idea is to have more than one well and have them interconnected with non-siphoning back-pressure or check valves in the likely event one well goes down. Your best practical advice on this subject is usually your local well driller. Do not purchase a ranch that does not have a reliable, safe and adequate water supply.

Climate: The climate is a consideration in the selection process only if you are willing and able to do something about it or provide for its ramifications and the occasional catastrophe. Of course, you can select an area where the climate agrees with you, such as the mountains, the desert area, the South with its humid areas or possibly the North with its winters. In an agronomic sense though, temperature, moisture and their cycles are important in determining the length of the growing season and the amounts of forage produced. It would be helpful to study the weather data for your prospective ranch to learn the average and extreme characteristics of the local climate. Memorable events such as droughts, floods, or hard winters need to be considered and planned for or else you may encounter a situation that would be almost intolerable. For example, if your ranch were subjected to frequent droughts it should contain irrigable land where feed may be raised to aid in carrying the cattle over such hard periods. It has been said by some experts that the southwestern and southern states have an advantage in a cow/calf enterprise because of the shorter and milder winters in these regions. The calves are usually born four to six weeks earlier than the northern calves and thus are larger and heavier when they are marketed the following fall. But in the end, in selecting a ranch, it will be mainly your personal preference for which climate is the most tolerable or enjoyable to you.

Ponds: Ponds, or "tanks" as they are called in some parts of the country, most notably in Texas, are one of the most pleasing, useful additions and investments you can make to your ranch. This amenity has an aesthetic property that adds value to the eye-appeal of the ranch, and may increase its values for water conservation and recreation. The pond also can provide water for fire protection, livestock, wildlife and supplemental irrigation.

It is not the purpose of this discussion to teach you how to build a pond but to point you in the right direction and impress upon you what a potent asset the pond is for you and your ranch. If your prospective ranch does not have a good water-holding tank or two now, we highly recommend you explore the possibility of building one. However, this is not a do-it-yourself venture. A good ranch pond did or will not come about by damming a gully. But if you understand the essential features of design and construction, and adhere to strict scientific and engineering principles, you can develop a most beautiful and enjoyable asset. You can obtain published information and competent technical assistance from the local offices of the Cooperative Extension Service or the Natural Resource Conservation Service. You may find that a cost-sharing plan is available to you through the USDA's Farm Service Agency. This well-respected agency was known for many years as the Agricultural Stabilization and Conservation Service. With the current state of "reinventing" government in Washington, we are not confident this long-admired and useful program will be available in the future. State conservation agencies, plus state and federal fish and wildlife agencies, can help you stock your pond with sport fish and give you detailed instructions for their maintenance.

A cardinal rule with ponds is to keep them filled with water so that the water level never fluctuates more than two feet. To do this you need an adequate source of water. If the pond is to be fed by a watershed, the area needs to be of a sufficient size to maintain the desired water level and yet not large enough to create a flood hazard. The size of the specific watershed should depend on the cubic size of the pond, the amount of rainfall, the evaporation rate for the area, watershed topography and use. It may be helpful to have a secondary source of water such as springs, artesian wells, or even drilled and pumped wells for times of drought or for topping-off purposes.

The size of the pond will depend on the available site, the water supply and the intended use. Ponds less than one acre in size are rarely successful. The depth should be at least twelve to fifteen feet. In addition, make sure the banks are fairly steep to avoid underwater areas with a depth of less than three feet. Shallow water encourages the growth of aquatic vegetation, which is unsightly and a nuisance. One of the secrets to a good pond is keeping it dark. This prevents the sunlight from reaching the bottom of the pond and encouraging plant growth. Darkness in the water is usually caused by microscopic organisms. These biologic entities are ingested by larger aquatic organisms which are then in turn eaten by fish. Thus, as in the production of your grass, your pond must contain sufficient fertility to support a fish population. If the water is not dark enough, fertilizer may have to be added to the tank. An old general rule is that if you can see your hand when your arm is immersed up to your elbow, you should add some fertilizer. Fertilizer recommendations are available from your extension service or the fish and wildlife people.

Final issues are the insurance and liability factors associated with the pond. The responsibility of the landowner varies in each state, but as a rule, deterrents like fences, gates, signs, life preservers and other safety equipment have a favorable impact on the liability issue. Finally, fire insurance rates also may be reduced because of the ranch pond. Check with your insurance company.

Improvements: You should inventory and note the condition of the improvements such as fences, corrals and buildings. Are the fences adequate to divide the ranch for proper grazing and are they stock-worthy? Are the corners of the barns or sheds square and the roof line straight? Are they well constructed? Are there utilities such as electric service, telephone and gas to where you want them and do these utilities have adequate capacity for your use? How are the internal roads built and what is their condition?

The condition of such infrastructure not only affects the value of the ranch, but if it is in good and serviceable shape, you, as the new owner, can focus your thoughts and energies on the many other factors needed for successful ranching.

Overinvestment in buildings and facilities entails a heavy and unnecessary financial charge against the ranch. Livestock, in general, do better outside, even in the winter, than in enclosed structures. The animals are thriftier, with less disease, and they are less costly to maintain. It is somewhat like the weekend cowboy in the warmer climates who buys a four-wheel-drive vehicle solely to drive to town on good hardtop highways—a waste of money, from the initial investment to the ongoing operating expenses. (They also extract a toll from our bodies with their more rigid suspensions.) Likewise with your livestock, save your money, let your cattle roam freely, and do them a favor—if your livestock needs shelter or shade, develop a nice patch of woods and spend more of your budget on the actual livestock, labor-saving equipment and roads.

Taxes and Use Controls: In selecting your ranch, it is important to consider the tax structure of the state as well as the taxes on the specific ranch property.

Real estate or property taxes are ad valorem taxes. This means they are levied according to the value of one's property, thus the more valuable the property, the higher the tax. Determining how much tax a property owner will be charged involves three basic steps: 1) the local government determines its budget and appropriation, 2) an appraisal is conducted of all taxable property within the taxation district, and 3) an allocation of the revenue that needs to be collected is devised for the individual property owners— hence, your property tax bill.

Aside from an academic interest, it is important for you to understand the specific real estate taxes for your prospective ranch. In the event you are not familiar with some terminology and mathematics, we offer the following abbreviated short course:

Appraised Value: Market value as determined by tax assessor or independent appraiser.

Assessed Value: A value placed on a property for the purpose of taxation.

Mill Rate: Property tax rate that is expressed in tenths of a cent per dollar of assessed valuation. Therefore, for calculation purposes it is helpful to remember that 1,000 mills equate to one dollar.

Example:

Given: Market value of $1,000/acre, assessment rate of 40%, mill rate of 50 for combined county and school assessment.

Therefore: $1,000 x 40% = $400 per acre = assessed value
$400 x 50 = 20,000 mills
20,000 mills ÷ 1,000 mills = $20/acre

The levy can also be expressed in two other ways: as dollars per hundred or per thousand of assessed valuation.

Dollars per hundred	Dollars per thousand
$5.00	$50.00

All these methods are used in the United States. If your ranch falls into the rural-urban fringe, your real estate assessment may be modified because of its agricultural use. In any event, you should check with your county tax office and the local school district to see if this helpful program is in effect in your area. It may have a dramatic influence on your tax bill as the ranch will be taxed on its use or income from agriculture. The method varies somewhat around the country and in some locations you may have to abide by some rules or standards to qualify.

Figure 3 is a true example of the impact of an "agricultural-use assessment." This property is an hour and a half northwest of Houston, Texas and consists of 73.13 acres and a 6,000-square-foot home. The property is used for horses and cattle.

Without Agricultural Classification

Parcel	Acres	Per Acre Value	Assessed Value	Tax Rate*	Tax
1	12.96	$2,350	$30,460	$1.90	$578.74
2	55.19	$1,880	$103,760	$1.90	$1,971.44
3	5.00	$3,010	$15,050	$1.90	$285.95
Residence		N/A	$229,770	$1.90	$4,365.63
Total Tax					$7,201.76

With Agricultural Classification

Parcel	Acres	Per-Acre Value	Assessed Value	Tax Rate*	Tax
1	12.96	$120.00	$1,560	$1.90	$ 29.64
2	55.19	$109.62	$6,050	$1.90	$114.95
3	5.00	$150.00	$ 750	$1.90	$14.25
Residence		N/A	$229,770	$1.90	$4,365.63
Total Tax					$4,524.47

Therefore:		
	Without agricultural classification	$7,201.76
	With agricultural classification	$4,524.47
	Savings	$2,677.29

* Dollars/hundred

Fig. 3. Comparison of Agricultural and Nonagricultural Tax Rates

If your home will be your main residence, you may want to declare it as your "homestead" in states where this exemption is permitted. There are also some legal benefits for this declaration.

Another consideration in your evaluation process is whether the prospective property has any use controls, zoning or other legal restrictions on your intended use. By going to the local government office you can determine if the ranch land is subject to a zoning ordinance, and if so, how it is zoned. Then you can determine your course of action.

Minerals and Water Rights: Always ask about the minerals when you are contemplating the purchase of a ranch. While it is true you usually get what you pay for, in areas where there is not intensive drilling activity, the seller will normally include at least fifty percent of the mineral interests that he owns. In fact, in the negotiating process you may actually obtain all the available minerals. One never knows how technology advances or new geologic ideas develop. One day, the area in question will have little or no interest from oil and gas exploration companies; the next, the area is overrun with geophysical activity and drilling rigs. An example of this phenomenon is in Washington County northwest of Houston, Texas, where oil and gas activity was relatively dormant, despite producing wells from a much earlier period. Unless one had producing minerals, the mineral interest almost always went with the sale of the surface acreage. Then, with the advent of new horizontal drilling techniques, a complete about-face took place. Almost anywhere in the county you can now see six to eight drilling rigs. Consequently, the mineral rights are essentially as valuable as the surface acreage.

Professor Miller has repeatedly reminded us that seeing producing oil and gas wells on the ranch always helped the bottom line of the ranching or purebred cattle business. One only needs to remember how the funds from Exxon's oil and gas program enabled the King Ranch to not only develop the Santa Gertrudis breed of cattle, win the Kentucky Derby and the Triple Crown with the popular horse Assault, but also enabled it to have one of the most sophisticated, attractive and extensive global beef cattle and horse operations in the world.

Water rights may come from a river, or be purchased from an irrigation district, or be from the aquifer below your ranch. In some states the water rights may be separated from the surface or there may be regional restrictions on their use. Water is becoming a serious agricultural problem as cities and urban developments tap increasing amounts of the available supply. In some areas, where irrigation is a necessity, it may be a critical issue in your selection process. Don't assume the water belongs to you or is not restricted in some way.

Existing Mortgage: Is there a mortgage on the property now? If so, can it be assumed, and what is the interest rate and the amortization schedule? If the answer is yes, and the terms are favorable, compare it to the financing package you can put together today for purchasing the ranch using current market rates and parameters. The current mortgage may be a built-in asset of the ranch.

Legalize

We cannot be your advisor relative to legal, estate and tax matters—you need the advice of licensed professionals. How you buy the ranch and the many issues related to its purchase, plus the purely technical nature of the rules of law, demand competent counsel. It is important to remember that real estate law has its origin in old English common law. This means it is based on the doctrine of court decisions, usage and custom. Therefore it may be different from some important aspects of the law with which you may be familiar. There may be variations in each state, but in general, the basic concept of English common law is followed. Matters such as form of ownership or the type of business ownership selected determine important issues from purchase through disposition of the property or business. Therefore, we strongly advise you to seek expert legal advice from a competent real estate attorney. From the financial and tax sides we suggest you have advice from an estate and/or tax expert such as a CPA who is experienced in these areas. This will not replace the need to use a good experienced and knowledgeable real estate broker. Use someone who has a knowledge of not only the prevailing prices of comparable properties but also the technical expertise of factors affecting agricultural production, such as soils, pastures and beef cattle, so he or she can help you investigate the selection criteria previously discussed. And we will share this bit of advice from distinguished Professor Neil Harl, of Iowa State University: "Don't sign any document unless you know what it will do for you or to you!"

There are two important areas relative to the purchase of a farm or ranch where we have had firsthand experience and deserve mention. The first involves the deal to purchase—it must be in writing—hence, a contract. If a problem is ever litigated, for any reason, you need a written and properly executed document or you will not get to first base. The second area involves the actual configuration of the land, which in most cases, determines the actual acreage. Do not believe the certified survey as the gospel—it may be fraudulent or the result of pure sloppiness. In most, if not all of the states, the recorded deed determines the actual description and boundaries of the property. Hence, competent professional advice and a good title policy issued by a financially reputable firm are essential.

To encourage you to be reasonably informed on the highly technical nature of a real estate transaction, we believe you should know the definitions and ramifications of the following key words. If not, look them up in reference material or ask your advisor.

Carry Over Basis	Life Interest
C Corporation	Limited Partnership
Community Property	Partnership
Deed of Trust	Personal Holding Company
Estate in Severalty	Right of Survivorship
EPA Report	Subchapter S
Future Interest	Tenancy by the Entireties
Income Tax Basis	Tenancy in Common
Installment Contract	Time is of the Essence
Joint Tenancy	Undivided Interest
Joint Venture	Unlimited Liability
Land Contract	

Remember to notify your insurance agent or carrier about a possible ranch purchase. Liability insurance must be updated. There are casualty and loss insurance policies available for your cattle herd, your buildings and your equipment. A ranch, while appearing tranquil most of the time, does have its share of accidents, so be prepared and protected with insurance coverage.

Financial Tidbits

Our first thought on this subject, above all else, is for the prospective rancher/buyer to develop a cash-flow budget. Seek competent advice if necessary, and use the budget as a management tool. Not only will it help you in your financing endeavors and operating program, it will also help you with the Internal Revenue Service in the event your tax return is challenged. Consider the use of credit as a productive resource much like you would good water and good soils, and incorporate credit into your business plan. For "do-it-yourselfers," there are some excellent computer software programs designed for home office use. The programs prompt you with questions about your anticipated business. They can help you generate a personalized business plan.

With the increase in land values and most other inputs associated with the ranching business, large amounts of capital are required. Even wealthy individuals may find it advantageous to use borrowed funds. The purpose of this section is to briefly examine the most common sources of credit for the ranching industry.

Financing the Ranch or Real Estate: It is generally believed that the largest source of ranch and farm real estate loans is from the sellers themselves. Sellers can finance the sale of their ranch using a land contract, deed of trust, mortgage or installment contract and may incur substantial financial and tax benefits. Buyers, on the other hand, usually obtain loan provisions that would not be possible from banks or other institutional lenders. Down payments and rates vary for a multitude of reasons, but generally are lower than one could obtain from institutional sources such as the Federal Land Bank, insurance companies or your personal bank.

The Federal Land Bank Association makes long-term loans secured by first liens on farm and ranch real estate for almost any agricultural purpose. The bank is authorized to make only sound loans and the maximum amount loaned will be a percentage of the appraised value, currently 85 percent or less of the real estate security. In addition, borrowers must buy stock in the local association that equates to $1,000 or 2 percent of the loan, whichever is less. Interest rates charged are closely tied to the rate of interest in the national money market; new loans are usually on a variable interest rate basis. An applicant for a loan applies at the local Federal Land Bank Association office serving the area where the subject property or ranch is located.

The Farmers Home Administration (FmHA) is a governmental agency operating under the United States Department of Agriculture. Its primary purpose is to make loans, at low interest rates, to farmers and ranchers who essentially cannot obtain credit from other sources. As with Federal Land Bank loans, applications should be initiated at the district FmHA office serving the area where the borrower's ranch is located.

Insurance companies provide another major source of ranch loans, particularly those that are considerably larger and longer term than those from other financial institutions. Because of the nature of their business they must have a diversified portfolio of low-risk investments, and agricultural real estate mortgages qualify. Most companies in most states can loan up to two-thirds of the appraised value of the property. Interest rates tend to follow the market for long-term funds. Insurance companies have field representatives in most agricultural areas and their degree of activity seems to fluctuate depending on the national economy.

Commercial banks also make real estate loans for the purchase of a ranch, but these are usually shorter in duration and smaller in size than the sources mentioned above. However, if you are a good customer of a bank, do not overlook this source of funding.

Financing Improvements and the Cow Herd: These are usually term loans from three to ten years used to construct improvements, such as barns and fences, or to purchase a herd of breeding cattle, expensive equipment, or for almost anything involved in the operation of a farm or ranch. Commercial banks and Production Credit Associations (PCA) dominate this field of non-real estate lending. Merchants and dealers may also extend credit for the purchase of equipment while many of the purebred and commercial sources of breeding stock and embryo transplants will usually finance at least a portion of your purchase. The latter is especially true if you are new in the business and your overall credit is good. The seedstock producers do it because it helps them get a new customer and one who, if satisfied, will return again. Historically, dealer credit normally commands a higher interest rate than banks. But today, as with the car industry, there are dealer incentives to help keep rates low. So shop around.

Financing Operating Expenses: Usually for seasonal needs, these loans are short-term and are the provenance of commercial banks, PCAs, or the FmHA. These funds should go for goods and services to be embodied in the product to be sold. The loan should be repaid at the end of the production period.

Don't be tempted to use short-term borrowed funds for the purchase of capital assets unless you have sufficient cash reserves or substantial non-ranch income. Short-term operational loans will usually require a complete financial statement and a cash budget. A full business plan will help both the process and your professional reputation immeasurably. Terms and rates vary greatly, so again, shop around.

Another federally chartered institution that will indirectly assist you in obtaining a mortgage for your ranch is the Federal Agricultural Mortgage Corporation, popularly known as Farmer Mac. It assists in developing and maintaining the secondary market for farm and ranch loans much as Fannie Mae and Ginnie Mae do for home mortgages. While operating within the Farm Credit System, it enables commercial banks, insurance companies, thrifts and Federal Land Banks to pool their agricultural real estate loans and sell them to investors. This provides liquidity in the farm and ranch real estate mortgage sector and a source of cash for lenders who adhere to Farmer Mac standards.

If you want information on farm loans and conservation programs look in the front of your telephone book for the Department of Agriculture under GOVERNMENT OFFICES—UNITED STATES for the office nearest you. You may also call 202-720-2791 in Washington, D.C., or use their Web site, www.usda.gov to obtain relevant information.

Personal Tidbits

We have been reminded by someone in the know, that there are at least two human resource and family concerns that need to be addressed for one to be a happy and financially successful weekend cowboy.

The first is to critically evaluate and select the best manager you can find and afford. Salary, per se, is often not the motivating factor from a manager's perspective. Location of the ranch, housing, the dedication of the owner for a worthwhile and credible program to purchase, breed and raise good beef cattle all play an important role in the manager's heart and mind, and ultimately, in his family's reception to your offer. And we cannot overemphasize the importance of a good manager. You must have confidence in the sound judgment and integrity of someone on the grounds. Your peace of mind, your reputation in the cattle industry, and, ultimately, your bank account's balance may depend upon it.

The second concern, if you have a family, is to ensure that there are outlets and activities that will stimulate the mind and body for all family members. One idea, if you are in the beef cattle breeding business, is to have your kids search, evaluate and select planned matings. Have them learn the economically important traits that you are looking for in your breeding program and encourage them to scan the enormous computerized data base of your breeders association for specific EPDs or Expected Progeny Differences. Then, with help from you and possibly the association's field representative, teach them the birds and the bees of the cattle business. Let them plan some matings based on progeny information, have them write down their reasons and predictions, and then have them

observe and critique the actual results. This system of reproductive analysis is technically called production testing. In order to be comprehensible by your children, be sure the characteristics are highly heritable and outwardly apparent or phenotypic, (See the section called  Genetics for the Layman). Make sure the traits can be measured objectively, such as polled, horned, color, inches, or pounds.

With such high-tech applications as computerized analyses and probabilities, genetic identification and mapping coupled with the practical biological necessities of life, a family project such as this would not only be educational, but challenging and exciting. It well could be exactly what one needs to keep the full family involved and happy.

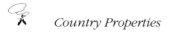

In addition, participating in the activities of the local historical society, antiquing, fishing, hunting, birding, learning to ride, participating in horse shows and the local 4-H showmanship programs for beef cattle, rabbits, etc.—all provide a means for the entire family to partake and enjoy your ranch or farm program. Only the creativity of your mind will define the limits.

Chapter 2

Type of Cattle Operation and Breed of Beef Cattle

The first section of this chapter will explore the type of cattle operation that would be feasible for the intended audience of this book. Later we will discuss the major breeds of beef cattle being raised in the United States.

There are many ways to classify beef cattle operations—full time, part time, cattle-grain combination, etc.—but for the purpose of this discussion we will classify the operation as commercial or registered. The commercial operation can be further subdivided as either a cow/calf or stocker program.

Commercial Cattle

Cow/Calf Operation: The commercial cow/calf operation usually consists of a mother cow and its calf from six to nine months after birth depending mainly on the season of birth, the geographic area of the country, and whether they will be sent directly to the feedlot or kept as stockers. The important fact is that the sale of the calves is the main product from this type of operation and its principal source of income. It is also important to note that a cow/calf operation is a relatively long-term investment program; significant time passes before the saleable product and income are realized. For example, once the program is started it takes approximately five to thirty months to develop a heifer that is suitable for sale or breeding. If she is bred, it then takes another fifteen to eighteen months before her calf is ready to market, thus an income stream may not begin for approximately three years. Can you sustain your operation during this time frame without getting discouraged and losing interest in the cattle business? If so, great! If not, you should not give up the urge to be a weekend cowboy. There are some ways to circumvent the problem. One is to start your program by purchasing bred-back cow/calf combinations. Naturally, this is more expensive for a productive unit, but the income stream starts much sooner. If you run your ranch as a competitive business based on scientific and business principles, you can plan for the future and not be surprised by the probable results. This usually makes for a much more enjoyable and profitable venture.

Stocker Operation: The stocker program is another way to accelerate income and cash flow in a commercial beef operation. It is defined as the time following weaning until the calves or steers are sold, put into the feedlot for finishing or put into a replacement heifer program. Stockers are young calves just weaned from their mothers, fed a non-finishing or low-energy ration and cared for in a more intensive manner. The growth and weight gain should be evaluated on the basis of available feed and its cost. Thus, a successful stocker operation usually has good pastures, harvested roughage such as high-value hay, silage or a winter small-grain rotation program. This type program is much more intensive than a cow/calf operation yet is more flexible, and as noted before, the income stream is greatly accelerated.

In our experience, the level of management necessary to make a profit is very critical in this type of program as factors such as estimating shrinkage, and the health and quality of the animal all greatly influence the economics of the operation. We know most of the experts who have written on the subject say otherwise, but we have done both a stocker and cow/calf operation, with a top management team, and for some reason the detailed care, observation, and health needs of young calves always take more management time and worry than a normal cow/calf operation.

Registered Cattle

The purebred or registered cattle business is a very specialized and highly refined form of the beef cattle production and marketing business. The animals in the herd are the offspring of individuals that are recorded in the herd book of an established national breed association and meet the requirements for registration. While the demands for capital, skill, good judgement and luck are extremely high, the opportunities and rewards are unlimited. However, in no other type of beef cattle operation does a high level of management play such an important role—you must either have it or make sure you obtain it!

To enter this exciting sector of the beef business, you must be dedicated to improving the specific breed of cattle you choose, be a patient and generous investor, have an inquisitive and visionary mind and above all, be an excellent salesman. In addition, you should enjoy, and actively participate in, the breed association's work and the social scene, such as cattle shows and sales. One of the secrets of making money in the purebred business is to "promote, promote, promote." What better person to do the promoting than you, the owner, with the guidance of your ranch manager and/or herdsman. Of course, you need traits in your herd that contribute to reproductive efficiency and carcass desirability. An impressive example of this was some years back when Peggy (Mrs. David) Rockefeller entered the purebred Simmental business. She was close to what one would call normal retirement age at the time and had a twenty-year business plan for the development of her new herd. We found her at the National Western Stock Show in Denver, outside in the pen area, with temperatures around zero to fifteen degrees Fahrenheit, promoting her cattle and trying to sell semen from one of her herd sires. This is an example of promotion, dedication, and arduous work resulting in production sales, some years later, bringing prices lovely to behold.

Today, we operate in a very exciting and challenging environment. The old scientific laws relating to heredity and the environment still prevail, and contribute solely to what you see as your end product or offspring. The traits we strive to improve remain:

1) reproductive performance or fertility;
2) mothering, or nursing ability;
3) rate of gain;
4) economy of gain;
5) longevity and
6) carcass grade and tenderness.

And yes, there are still 50,000 to 100,000 genes on thirty pairs of chromosomes which control the above traits, but we now have such techniques as ova transfers, genome mapping, sex determination, and even a process to transfer a nucleus from a developing embryo into an unfertilized egg. As we write this, a researcher has transferred the genes from a mature cell into an unfertilized egg and "reprogrammed" the development of the cell into an identical offspring, a process commonly referred to as cloning. This was done with a sheep but one can imagine a similar technique will be developed for beef cattle. And now, in the closing days of 1998, researchers have reported the successful cloning of calves from the cells of a single adult cow. In addition, computer analysis for EPDs (Expected Progeny Differences), ultrasound and other reproductive and production enhancements are commonplace. With this new arsenal of technology, we can not only cut short the time frame it takes to develop a top purebred herd but also accelerate and define more clearly the changes in our product. With a little luck, a lot of money, and a high degree of management, one may reduce this time frame from a lifetime or two, to possibly a decade.

We were raised and indoctrinated with the principle to develop a significant, meaningful and famous purebred beef herd, one had to have a sire of national reputation and recognition. This philosophy still exists, to some extent, because of the practical nature of the cattle business and the use of purebred bulls for upgrading commercial beef cattle herds. However, with the new technologies and the fact that, with minor exceptions, each offspring receives half of its inheritance from the sire and half from the dam, one may now focus upon the maternal side of the breeding equation and thereby bring true fame to a herd because of its female family.

Major Beef Breeds in the United States

One really needs to run for cover when a discussion of breeds of beef cattle and their specific values begins. "Politically correct" in this context has much merit; however, we believe it is safe to say that essentially all breeds have something to contribute or they would not exist for long. Try to keep an open mind. Don't be smitten with fads; and do not rely on tradition. The old saying, "Do not be the first to try the new or the last to throw the old away," is apropos with respect to making a large investment in the purebred cattle business.

Our suggestions on selecting a breed of cattle are: 1) observe what types of cattle are in your area, 2) visit ranchers who raise registered cattle, 3) attend production sales and livestock shows, 4) know the people associated with a particular breed, 5) recognize what good cattle look like, 6) write to the purebred breed associations for their literature and help, 7) talk to the beef cattle extension specialist and county agricultural agent of your state university system, and 8) find a well-respected breeder in your area to be your mentor.

When we first entered the registered Simmental business in Texas we were fortunate to have Albert "Tito" West of San Antonio and his family to guide us. They were our "sponsors"—they were impeccably honest, knowledgeable and pointed us in the right direction—from blood lines to pricing advice on purchases to marketing. They even made sure we were included in the "social network" of the cattle business. When we eventually sold the business they made it an enjoyable and profitable event. We can not overemphasize the importance of an open mind, thorough deliberation and the advice of a respected confidant or mentor when one contemplates becoming a weekend cowboy.

Therefore, without much editorial comment we present most of the breeds of beef cattle being raised in the United States today. You may write to their respective breed associations (listed in the Appendix) for specific information on the breed and breeders in your area. Be inquisitive and the breed you fall in love with, figuratively speaking, will be the best one for you.

Angus: This breed was imported from Scotland over a century ago and today over 10 million head have been recorded. It is recognized as being very refined, completely black and without horns, or "polled," as this trait is called in the industry. Meat packers and consumers have always had a favorable image, if not love affair, of the Angus breed. The American Angus Association has exploited this relationship with a Certified Angus Beef Program that encourages the consumer to purchase certified Angus cuts. This program has grown from approximately 17 million pounds sold in 1985 to approximately 410 million pounds in 1998. This is another example of the rewards of promotion as certified Angus beef can now be found in all states and in more than thirty-three countries. Angus is one of the major breeds of beef cattle in the United States today. The Angus breed association records more cattle each year than any other breed association making it the largest beef breed registry in the world. It is represented by both registered and commercial herds throughout most of the country.

Beefmaster: This breed was developed in the United States approximately 90 years ago. Hereford, Shorthorn, and Brahman cattle were systematically crossed until today the purebred Beefmaster is one-quarter Shorthorn, one-quarter Hereford and one-half Brahman. Thus, when Beefmasters are crossed on Beefmasters, or on true F_1 Brahman cows, you will always have 50 percent English blood in your calves. The breed, which does not have a uniform color, is bred and selected on 1) weight, 2) conformation, 3) fertility, 4) milking ability, 5) hardiness and 6) disposition. An interesting sidelight is that to ensure quality control, cattle are inspected and approved for breed character and conformation by an association representative before they are issued registration certificates. This is in addition to the association's performance initiative which it calls the Weights and Measures Program. Hall-of-Fame pitcher Nolan Ryan now pitches the virtues of his Beefmasters and the breed association's (BBU) new E-6 program.

Belgian Blue: This breed originated in Southern Belgium in the early 1900s as a dual purpose breed. Because of its heavy muscular characteristics, the beef trait was developed and today it is used in a crossbreeding program by beef breeders and dairymen. The breed is recognized by its rounded outline and prominent muscles. Their color can be white, blue roan or sometimes black. There is an American breed association that promotes those traits of the animal that satisfy the demand for leaner and healthier beef.

Blonde d'Aquitaine: The Blondes, as they are referred to in the industry, are a solid color, closely resembling wheat, and were imported in 1972 from France, where they are the third largest beef breed. They are used in this country as a cross to obtain leaner beef. They have an American breed association which serves as the official registry, collects data from performance tests and maintains a standard for breeding, shows and sales.

Braford: This breed was developed approximately fifty years ago in the United States to take advantage of the reputed benefits of Brahman blood in the humid areas of the South. In all instances, the germ plasm is a combination exclusively of Hereford and Brahman blood lines. The purebred and registered Braford is usually three-eighths Brahman and five-eighths Hereford, but the registry permits some latitude in the relative proportion of each. The Braford industry has a new breeders association formed in 1994. It currently focuses its breeding and promotional efforts on the commercial market.

Brahman: This breed is characterized as having animals with a large hump on the shoulder and long droopy ears. Zebu-type cattle were imported into the United States from India, when the original British imported cattle, which dominated the American beef industry for many years, were thought to be unsatisfactory to some cattlemen in the South. Many breeders and cattlemen believed the British breeds were less tolerant to heat, insects and parasites and, in addition, thought the cattle did not like the coarse tropical-type grass available then. While the Zebu breeds, of which there are about six, performed better in the South, their carcass and reproduction traits were unsatisfactory for the U.S. market. The American Brahman was created from several Indian Zebu breeds imported into this country. This breeding resulted in a breed which proved quite useful in the southern United States. In fact, many thought crosses between the British and the Brahman breeds met needs better than purebreds of either type. A surprising number of the major breeds today such as Brangus, Beefmaster, Braford, Charbray, Simbrah, and Santa Gertrudis, were the result of this crossing, while much of the commercial cattle in the South contain some Brahman blood. Regardless of the fad of packers at one time or another, the availability of this reservoir of genetic material has been constructive to the U.S. beef industry.

Brangus: This breed, developed in the United States almost fifty years ago, combines the best traits of the Brahman and Angus breeds. The Brahman is noted for their resistance to disease and insects, overall hardiness and maternal instincts, while the Angus is most noted for its carcass qualities. The breed is solid black, naturally polled and is typically short-haired. Registered Brangus are three-eighths Brahman or Zebu breeding and five-eighths Angus. They have a larger, more drooping ear and more looseness of hide than Angus cattle but we must admit when we first visited Willow Springs Ranch and saw Dr. & Mrs. Gardner's high-quality herd of purebred Brangus twenty-five years ago, our first thought was that they were high-lineage Angus cattle. And we were not alone! Today, blood analysis would substantiate their heritage. The breed has been exceptionally promoted through the years by both the breed association and the many prominent breeders.

Braunvieh: Developed in the mountain valleys of Switzerland where today roughly 40 percent of cattle are of this breed. They are now found in most countries of the world, from the Arctic Circle to the Tropics. More than one hundred head were imported into the United States between 1869 and 1880, and became the basis of the American Brown Swiss dairy breed. From 1968 to 1985, bulls and females were imported into the United States but were selected in Europe for beef production. The Braunvieh Association of America was formed in 1984. The animals have brown hair. Adult females weigh between 1,200 to 1,500 pounds; adult males tip the scales between 2,100 to 2,500 pounds. They are promoted mainly for their excellent maternal traits.

Charbray: Essentially a Charolais Brahman cross, standardized at the five-eighths to three-eighths ratio. The registry for the breed is under the fold of the American International Charolais Association.

Charolais: Charolais is one of the several breeds of ancient French cattle and was first imported into the United States in 1936 by the King Ranch. Because of the quarantines against hoof-and-mouth disease further imports were prohibited. Not until the mid 1960s did new blood arrive in the States. Prior to this, breeding up was the only program available. All Charolais-based breeds are represented by the American International Charolais Association. One of the most educational and informational pieces of free literature about the beef cattle industry is published by this association and is titled, "The Young Cattleman." While it is aimed at the juniors it is worthwhile reading for any newcomer entering the beef cattle business. The purebred are recognized by their distinctive white or off-white hair and light pigmentation. There are approximately 1.5 and 2.0 million head of registered Charolais in the United States.

Chiangus: A composite breed that contains no less than one-eighth nor more than three-fourths Chianina. The balance must be Angus. Chiangus must be polled or scurred and may have white only on the underline.

Chianina: This breed, pronounced "kee-a-nee-na," originated in the province of Tuscany in Central Italy. The fullblood Chianina range in color from white to steel grey and have black-pigmented skin. Originally, only semen was brought into the United States, but in 1975 fullbloods were imported into the U.S. through the Italy-Canada channel. The Chianina are very large and are used primarily for crosses which are viewed favorably in the feedlot. American purebred Chianina must be seven-eighths Chianina, or more.

Gelbvieh: Pronounced "Gelp-fee," the American Gelbvieh Breeders Association was formed in 1971 with the importation of semen from Germany, the mother country of the breed. The association maintains a large database of performance records, which are mandatory for registration, and result in an Annual Sire Summary, Cow Recognition Program and EPDs for all registered Gelbvieh. The breed is promoted as the "Mother Breed of Beef" by emphasizing rapid early growth, lean yield, fertility, milk production, and maternal efficiency. The breed has an active association and if you write them for information you will be impressed with the speed of their response.

Hereford: This breed was imported from England more than a century ago. It is easily recognized by its unique color pattern. This pattern of white face, red body with white markings on the crest, brisket, underline and switch give it a valuable trademark which is used and promoted in the industry. The Hereford is one of the major breeds of beef cattle in the United States today and can be found throughout the country in purebred and commercial herds.

Limousin: This breed is one of the fine beef breeds in Europe. Its heritage can be traced back for many centuries to the Limoges region of France where it was known as the "butcher's animal." It was initially imported to North America in 1968 and now is found in most states and provinces of Canada. In the past it was easily recognized by its beautiful golden color, but, as has happened with other breeds, man has tinkered with the formula for color, and we now have black purebred Limousin—ostensibly from their breeding-up program. Their herd book or registry is maintained by the North American Limousin Foundation. Incidentally, the association has a nice pamphlet entitled "Select a Winner" which would be helpful to new weekend cowboys and members of their family.

Maine-Anjou: This breed originated and developed in the northwestern part of France and derives its name from the Maine and Anjou River Valleys. The first Maine-Anjou cattle were imported into Canada in 1969 and semen ultimately entered the United States for its breeding-up program. In France this breed was recognized as being relatively large and having a lovely, deep-red color with sprinklings of white. Today in the United States there is a tendency to develop the color black into the breed. We said we would not editorialize but on this we can not resist: We think it is a shame to take a breed with its traditional beautiful and characteristic color and change it for no biological reason. Although, in their defense, there is a perception in the industry, and confirmed by some studies, that black-hided cattle bring a premium in the market. In any event, there is a breeder's association that may enlighten you.

Marchigiana: Called "Marky" for convenience and ease of promotion, this breed of cattle is popular in Italy. Semen was first imported into the United States in 1974, and in the fall of 1996, cattlemen started to import both new semen and embryos from Europe. There is a small, but active, American breed association which promotes the Marky as having excellent feed-conversion ability, high daily average gains, and large rib eyes.

Murray Grey: This breed, developed in Australia in the early 1900s, is the result of a light roan Shorthorn-Angus cross. The resultant calves were all grey in color and were the basis for the breed. Today it is Australia's most popular beef breed. Semen was imported into the States in 1969 and now the breed and its crosses are found in most areas of the country. There is an active breeder's association promoting its cattle as the most efficient and finishing breed in the world.

Piedmontese: This unique breed originated and developed in the Piedmont area of Italy. It is unique because the breed carries the double muscle gene and is used quite extensively in Europe for crossbreeding with dairy cows. It is ironic in some ways because beef cattle experts shied away from double muscling but with current demands for so-called leaner and healthier beef, the breed has attracted interest in the United States for crossbreeding programs. The adult animals are recognized with grey-white hair and black skin pigmentation while the calves are fawn-colored. The first imports arrived in North America in 1980; in 1984 an American breeders association was formed.

Pinzgauer: This breed has its origin in the Pinz Valley of Austria and can be distinguished by its unique coloring. They have a lovely chestnut brown color on their sides with a white topline and underline along with orange around the eyes and udder. Pinzgauer are horned, highly fertile and considered good foragers. They have both an American and Canadian breeders association.

Polled Hereford: This distinct breed with its own herd book was developed in the United States from horned Hereford cattle that had a genetic mutation relative to their horn trait. Cattle with such polled traits were bred together and ultimately such systematic breeding laid the foundation for the Polled Hereford breed.

Today, a very popular breed, and one which has essentially the same characteristics as the Hereford, except it is polled. As we write this the Polled Hereford Association has consolidated with the American Hereford Association with the latter name surviving. There is now only one breed journal: *Hereford World*.

Red Angus: This breed shares the same origin as the Black Angus and is genetically the same except that now, through systematic selection, it carries the homozygous recessive gene pair for the color red. (See the section on genetics, Chapter Seven.) This genetic characteristic has the advantage of always producing red offspring when bred to Red Angus or any other red breed. Since they are naturally polled (hornless), which is a dominant trait, all breeding of the Red Angus result in offspring with the polled characteristic.

We believe this breed was helped tremendously by a well-known and talented Black Angus breeder, Jim Leachman, of Ankony Farms fame, who later promoted this breed in the West. The breeder's association was one of the first to require complete performance records on the total herd. Along with their Total Herd Reporting program it now promotes the breed as being typical Angus but with the additional benefit that the red color reflects sunlight better than black and thus the animals are less susceptible to heat, pink eye, cancer eye, and sunburned udders.

Red Brangus: This breed developed originally from a purebred white Brahman and black Angus cross where the Angus was heterozygous for polledness and black color. The offspring were interbred and selected for the red color. The breeders at the time thought the red coloring would help them with pink eye and cancer eye. Because of the need for a recessive gene pair to get the color red, the offspring eventually would all be red, which would give the herd uniformity and thus a promotional tool. The breed is similar to the Brangus in all other traits but they have a separate herd book and association.

Red Poll: This breed was imported in the latter half of the nineteenth century from England and became quite popular in the United States as a dual-purpose breed. Today the breed association stresses maternal traits and current breeders select for beef-type conformation. As the name implies they are polled and have an attractive medium to deep rich red color.

Romagnola: An old-line breed from the mountains of Italy, which recently has been introduced into the United States. They are being promoted for crossbreeding programs, and their apparent ability to adapt to tropical and subtropical climates is very good. In the grass-fed Latin American market they are frequently crossed with Zebu types.

Salers: This breed, pronounced Sa'lair, is an ancient breed from central France. This long ancestry is considered one of the reasons that the breed has a marked positive effect on inheritance in crossbreeding programs. The first imports into the United States came in 1975 and during the last twenty years the breed has established itself throughout North America. The breed association promotes the Salers as the "Balanced Breed." From recent observations we believe the breed is making inroads in the crossbreeding market. Originally a beautiful mahogany, we have seen some polled black Salers in the last few years, the result of Angus blood somewhere in their breeding-up or crossbreeding programs. The breed association collects and offers much data relative to breeding traits and currently is emphasizing carcass traits such as marbling score, carcass weight, fat thickness and rib eye area in the event cattle are paid on a carcass-value basis.

Santa Gertrudis: The modern Santa Gertrudis is deep cherry red and carries approximately five-eighths Shorthorn and three-eighths Brahman blood. The name comes from the Santa Gertrudis land grant which was originally issued by Spain and on which the breed developed. The King Ranch of South Texas not only started the original crossings, but for many years controlled the development of the breed by refusing to sell females. Ultimately the breed prevailed on its own merits and now it is found in numbers throughout the South and most semitropical and tropical countries of the world. The breeders association maintains an open herd book so that new bloodlines may be introduced. Today, the King Ranch is developing a composite breed called "Santa Cruz" which has a strong dose of Santa Gertrudis blood. This combination is one-half Santa Gertrudis, one-fourth Red Angus, and one-fourth Gelbvieh.

Theoretically this infusion should help with maternal and carcass-quality traits.

Senepol: This breed was developed in the Virgin Islands in the 1920s with Red Poll and N'Dama blood. Senepol are a solid red color with no horns. Only during the last decade have they been imported into the United States. The breed has suffered until relatively recently from the lack of promotion by a major beef cattle breeder or innovator. Today the breeders association is promoting the positive aspects of the "heat tolerant/tender beef" question. The cattle themselves are considered heat and insect tolerant and highly fertile.

Shorthorn: This breed was imported from England more than two centuries ago and has always been held in high esteem. Later, advanced Scottish breeding encouraged a movement away from the strictly English blood type. Today Scottish breeding is synonymous with Shorthorn cattle around the world. Earlier in this century the breed was probably the most popular of the beef breeds but lately with strong competition from other breeds it has lost its popularity. The breed is usually recognized because of its red and roan color. Much Shorthorn blood exists in crossbred cattle today but purebred or registered herd numbers are on the decline. The association has embarked on an active promotion campaign for the future including its Certified Shorthorn Beef Program. The herd book, formed in 1846, contains both horned and polled cattle.

Simbrah: This breed is a combination of two of the most popular breeds of cattle in the world, the Brahman/Zebu, which ranks number one, and Simmental, which is second. These two breeds with genetically divergent backgrounds and different strengths, when combined, should maximize dominant hybrid vigor. The breed association contends that when combining the strength of the Brahman breed (longevity, heat tolerance, disease and insect resistance, durability, grazing ability, and calving ease) with excellent traits from the Simmental (fertility, milking ability, rapid growth, and early sexual maturity) an excellent opportunity exists for a most useful offspring. A purebred Simbrah consists of five-eighths Simmental and three-eighths Brahman, whereas other combinations, with a minimum of three-eighths Simmental and one-fourth Brahman, are considered a "Percentage Simbrah." Both are eligible for registration if all the additional requirements are met. Both polled and horned traits exist in the breed and no discrimination is practiced against either.

Simmental: This breed is one of the oldest and most widely distributed groups of cattle in the world. Since its origin in Switzerland, the breed has spread to all six continents and its numbers are estimated between 40 and 60 million. In Continental Europe the breed is composed of several different strains: in Switzerland it is known as Simmental; in France it's Abondance, Monebeleard and Pie Rouge de L'est; in Germany and Austria it's Fleckvieh. While there possibly was some importation of Simmental cattle into the United States in the 19th century, the breed did not grow and flourish in this country until the famed French bull, Parisien, was imported from France in 1967. The breed is now the third largest beef breed in the United States. During 1995, approximately 100,000 Simmental and Simbrah calves were registered with the American Simmental Association (ASA). In their first sire summary (the first produced by a beef breed association in the United States), ASA evaluated thirteen purebred bulls. In a more recent sire summary, ASA evaluated almost 23,000 purebred Simmental and 420 Simbrah bulls. The breed has experienced tremendous growth and acceptance in all phases of the U.S. beef industry. Because there was a great interest in the polled trait in North America, the dominant polled character has been highly developed and maintained by careful selection in a large number of purebred Simmental and Simbrah herds.

Texas Longhorn: The ancestors of this breed, with its rich history and long horns, originally came from Spain to Texas via Mexico. These animals survived without the benefit of man and developed traits of their own by true natural selection. Traits such as hardiness, disease resistance, longevity, fertility, and browse utilization worked well for them. The Texas Longhorn became the financial salvation of the Southwest. An estimated 10 million Texas cattle were trailed to northern markets between 1866 and 1895 bringing in approximately $200,000,000. However, because of fencing the open range and the importation of new breeds, the Texas

Longhorn was almost extinct in the early 1900s. Renewed interest resulted in the formation, in 1964, of the Texas Longhorn Breeders Association. The Association promotes the breed by emphasizing the characteristics developed during the early years in America and by working to preserve the blood and tradition of these unique cattle. Today, approximately 250,000 head of Texas Longhorn cattle have been registered.

Wagyu: The word *Wagyu*, sounding like a dish at a Japanese restaurant, actually refers to all Japanese beef cattle. *Wa* means "Japanese" and *gyu* means "cattle." There are two substrains, one being red and the other black. Through a century of amalgamation of Brown Swiss, Devon, Shorthorn, Simmental, Ayshire, Korean, Holstein and Angus blood, the current Wagyu type exists. Original importation of these cattle into the U.S. was in 1976. There is an active American breed association that emphasizes the meat quality of the breed.

Part Two:

Operating the Ranch

Chapter 3

Trying to Make a Go of It

Current Economics

We are at our wits' end trying to write a rational story about the economics of the cattle business. Recently, corn was $9.10/cwt., soybeans $13.65/cwt., wheat $11.00/cwt. and grain sorghum or milo was around $8.50/cwt. The prices of these animal feeds determine, to some extent, the number of cattle in feed lots and ultimately affect the price and number of live cattle. This gives rise to the well-talked-about, but true, cattle cycle. With per-capita red meat consumption on the wane and the current escalated value of animal feed, it is sometimes difficult to make money in segments of the cattle cycle. For example, feeder cattle were recently selling for as low as 50 cents per pound and live cattle (commercial) around $57.00 per hundredweight. Put that into your computer and see what spits out—blood!

Better yet, become an economist and look at trends, cycles and other curvy things. It certainly will make you feel better and you may even find some interesting data which you may incorporate into your business plan. In fact you may be lucky and outsmart or outguess the majority to make a small fortune. Indeed, the outlook in the latter part of 1997 is improving as cattle prices have increased and grain prices have receded from their recent highs. In any event, the point we want to make in this chapter is that the ranching/beef business is an extremely challenging one. The experts claim that an average return on a beef cattle operation would be from two to five percent on invested capital. If one could be assured of this return, life would be a lot less traumatic for both the full-time rancher and weekend cowboy. Unfortunately, in some years even this return is unattainable.

Avenues to Increase Profitability

A lot of contributing factors out of one's control influence the bottom line of this type of enterprise. However, by controlling and properly managing certain aspects of the business, you will have a much better chance for a profitable venture. You know the old saying, "Keep your eye on the ball!"

To illustrate this point, we are going to use a current real-life example which we personally know quite well. It is a good example because the ranch management uses all the tools available to them. We will disregard the investment value of the real estate while focusing on the operational aspects of the ranch. The setting is a 4,000-acre ranch located approximately forty miles outside of a major metropolitan area in Texas. The soils and other agronomic factors are considered excellent and the management is of a very high standard. The current cattle program involves a purebred registered cattle herd along with a commercial cow/calf operation. They try to maintain a workable 2,000 mother cow herd on the property and the calves are currently sold after weaning. The ranch is managed professionally for an absentee, but involved owner. The cash operating statement for the past year is shown in figure 4. Note the line items, you can use these categories as a start in your business plan.

Overall, the results are quite good when one considers the deteriorating state of the cattle market. Even so, the losses are not a healthy situation, both financially and emotionally. From a management standpoint, what can be done to improve the profitability of this operation? The answers will glide us over the recommended methods for improving the profitability of most beef cow/calf operations. And remember, no matter how good you think you are, there is always room for improvement.

	Total	Per Acre	Per Cow Unit
Revenues			
Cattle Sales	$948,000.00	$237.00	$474.00
Other	30,000.00	7.50	15.00
Total Revenues	978,000.00	244.50	489.00
Expenses			
Cost of Sales	40,000.00	10.00	20.00
Salaries & Benefits	295,000.00	73.75	147.50
Feed	154,000.00	38.50	77.00
Seed & Fertilizer	191,000.00	47.75	95.50
Pesticides	32,000.00	8.00	16.00
Veterinary Services	61,000.00	15.25	30.50
Farm Supplies	25,000.00	6.25	12.50
Breeding	4,000.00	1.00	2.00
Show & Sale	30,000.00	7.50	15.00
Trucking	1,000.00	0.25	0.50
Travel	3,000.00	0.75	1.50
Utilities	52,000.00	13.00	26.00
Fuel (Gas & Oil)	30,000.00	7.50	15.00
Advertising	5,000.00	1.20	2.50
General Insurance	38,000.00	9.50	19.00
Property Taxes	40,000.00	10.00	20.00
Legal Fees	2,000.00	0.50	1.00
Payroll Fee	2,000.00	0.50	1.00
Equipment Rental	2,000.00	0.50	1.00
Office Supplies	2,000.00	0.50	1.00
Miscellaneous	14,000.00	3.50	7.00
Total Expenses	$1,023,000.00	$255.70	$511.50
Operating Income	$(45,000.00)	$(11.20)	$(22.50)

Fig. 4. Sample cash operating statement for the hypothetical ranch.

With respect to this particular scenario there are eight general avenues to increase profitability.

The first avenue is to reduce total cost without changing the percent calf crop, weaning weight or price of sale cattle. It has been our observation that in most businesses, including agribusiness, one first reviews and attacks the side of the ledger where one is most experienced or familiar, i.e. production people tend to look at costs while marketing types look for ways to increase revenues. In this particular case, the expenses had been thoroughly reviewed and already cut substantially the prior year. Although some particular line items may look high for a family-run operation, some, such as property taxes, we can do little about. Furthermore, the operation is a cohesive unit; at this time we deemed it better to look at how to increase revenues with little or no increase in cost.

The second avenue is to increase the herd size. The principle applied here is to improve efficiency with better utilization of existing land, pastures and improvements. There is ample pasture and forage available to increase the cow herd by 50 percent or 1,000 cows or their equivalent, which the current management could readily do. While there will be some increase in feed, pesticides and veterinary charges, the overall increase in revenue and resultant income would be significant. An alternative would be to turn the extra supply of grass into a cash crop. At times there is a dilemma between the underutilization of pastures, on one hand, and overstocking on the other, when lack of rain creates a shortfall in available forage. But this is where good management plays an important role.

The third avenue would be to increase the weaned calf crop. Some ranchers talk of a 95 percent calf crop but in reality settle for 85 percent or less. The point here is to strive for the best—use 95 percent as the base or minimum acceptable percentage. And in this analysis one should be sure to use all the cows and heifers of breeding age in the herd—not just the ones that actually calved. This will provide a more intellectually honest and correct picture of the reproductive performance of the herd.

The fourth avenue would be to increase the weaning weights of the calves. Weaning weights are also under the rancher's control as this trait is moderately heritable. So use bulls and cows that have and can handle the higher EPDs for this trait. In addition, make sure the calf has adequate nutrition, a high degree of health and possibly use implants and supplemental feeding.

The fifth avenue is to produce better cattle. Again, this is a highly heritable trait, especially with respect to the carcass and is under the rancher's control. Better quality cattle bring better prices. A change in the higher grades can mean an increase in price of $50 or more per head in the commercial sector.

The sixth avenue is to review how and when you sell your cattle. Do you promote your ranch and breeding program? Is the calving program synchronized so you can sell the end product into a favorable market—one that may be contrary to the masses.

The seventh avenue is to increase the carrying capacity per acre by intensified pasture management. This enhancement involves the proper and probably increased use of fertilizer, the change to improved forage species, a more conscientious weed control program, and finally, the reevaluation and possible improvement of the grazing system. For example, the use of winter, or in reality, early spring pastures of wheat, oats or ryegrass will substantially increase the availability of high-quality pastures. Its use should be considered in relation to the feed requirements of the herd and the cost of nutrients from other sources such as hay. This is sometimes related to the second avenue—increase the herd size—as it provides for a greater utilization of pastures.

The eighth avenue is to explore the possibility of becoming an integrated beef producer by 1) selling extended growth period type calves or steers directly to the feeder, 2) selling feed cattle directly to the packer or 3) selling the finished products on a grade and yield basis.

When we examine the above methods to improve profitability for this ranch, we find there are realistically only two avenues for improved performance. The major one is to increase the size of the cow herd and the other is to attempt to produce a better grade animal. On the surface it looks like the old proverb, "Lose on every unit but make up for it on volume." Since they are already losing approximately $22 per cow unit, if they substantially increase the cow herd, their losses should, theoretically, also increase. But in fact we are counting on increased efficiency/production from current ranch inputs to lower operating costs per unit of production, whether it be an acre or a cow/calf unit, and the following summary demonstrates this principle.

Current   2,000-unit cow herd

Revenues	$978,000.00
Cash expenses	$1,023,000.00
Operating income	$(45,000.00)
Per acre	$(11.25)
Per cow unit	$(22.50)

Expanded   3,000-unit cow herd

Current revenues	$978,000.00
Improved methods	
1st avenue	—
2nd avenue	$430,000.00
3rd avenue	—
4th avenue	—
5th avenue	$30,000.00
6th avenue	—
7th avenue	—
8th avenue	—
Improved revenues	$1,438,000.00
Increased cash expenses	$1,120,000.00
Operating income	$318,000.00
Per acre	$79.50
Per cow unit	$106.00

Fig. 5. Financial improvement from increased efficiencies and better cattle.

The above numbers do not reflect the cost of money nor non-cash items such as depreciation. We have purposely ignored the cost of land because most readers will be looking for, and purchasing ranch property in areas relatively close to urban centers. Thus the cost of real estate has no realistic bearing on its intrinsic value for agriculture or ranch use. Ironically, past experience has demonstrated that such settings usually enable people to cash out profitably when they no longer want to be a weekend cowboy. In fact, you should include the increase in land values in your financial analysis to compare various land parcels. Without getting into highly-technical accounting techniques, if you prepare a business plan, and we strongly urge you to do so, include a discounted cash flow model for your investment.

Credit and its Influence

While we mention rates of return, we will briefly discuss the judicious use of credit and how it influences your return on invested capital. Credit is a two-edged sword as it can cut through many obstacles when the market, weather and other operational matters are going well, but it can "cut you into pieces," when things go bad. For both a full-time or weekend cowboy, our advice is this: Don't borrow unless you have a sure way to service the debt. Assuming you do, the next positive criteria you will need is to make sure the rate of return of your investment is higher than the interest rate on your loan. If this can be answered in the affirmative, your net earnings will be enhanced.

Do not be tricked into the philosophy that borrowing always increases your rate of return or net earnings. Again, only when the rate of return of your ranching operation is greater than the interest rate of your loan is this so. With loan rates not usually going below 8 percent, while going upwards to 21 percent just more than a decade ago, you must be very critical in your analysis to borrow. Remember, it takes a good operator in the ranching business to average a 5 percent return in a normal year. When special circumstances or the cattle market foretell an exceptional year in the offing, then it may be prudent to leverage yourself to a higher degree.

A few simple but important examples show this phenomenon.

Example 1: The investment in ranch, cattle, etc. is $1,000,000. The three cases are: no borrowing, 50 percent borrowed and 75 percent borrowed capital. If the interest rate is 10 percent and the internal rate of return for the ranch is 5 percent, then the following would happen:

	Case 1	Case 2	Case 3
	No borrowing	50% borrowed	75% borrowed
Equity	$1,000,000	$500,000	$250,000
Loan	—0—	$500,000	$750,000
Earnings	$50,000	—0—	$(25,000)

The interest rate is higher than the internal rate of return for the ranch so the all-equity or no-borrowing case will be the only scenario to have net earnings. But you can also see the damaging effect of credit at the other end of the chart. Case three shows a loss for the 75 percent loan. This loss will then be deducted from equity and you can see that if this type of borrowing continues without an increase in the rate of return, in a number of years, little equity will remain.

Example 2: Assume that the weather is good and there are excellent pastures. Cattle prices are high, resulting in an internal rate of return of 15 percent. If we use the same capital, borrowing and interest rate as above, the following would happen:

	Case 1	Case 2	Case 3
	No Borrowing	50% Borrowed	75% Borrowed
Equity	$1,000,000	$500,000	$250,000
Loan	—0—	$500,000	$750,000
Earnings	$150,000	$100,000	$75,000

Now all three scenarios make money because the ranch generates a return that is greater than the interest rate. This example also shows the positive effects of leverage on the rate of return. The rate of return for invested capital in case one is 15 percent, for case two it is 20 percent, while in case three it is 30 percent.

One argument made for leverage is that if you sell the ranch for substantially more than your investment in it, you may significantly increase your rate of return by borrowing—and it should be taxed at a favorable capital gains rate. But recognize that sometimes the real estate market becomes depressed and prices do fall—as many ranchers and farmers in our heartland found out approximately a decade ago. Additionally, real estate investments are relatively illiquid, so maintaining a current discounted cash flow forecast, and practicing prudence, will pay off.

One point to remember: the interest rate is a variable in real life and you should account for it at the prevailing rates.

In summary, we have tried to describe the most important economic facets of the cattle/ranching business—or at least the ones over which you have some control. All will influence your operations in some way, but not all may be of major importance to your specific operation.

Chapter 4

Eye Appeal and Investment Considerations

In 1999, common stocks reached at an all-time high; the Dow-Jones Industrials were over 11,000 and there seemed to be no let up in demand for equities. Many commodities were also experiencing important lows after setting all-time highs, and this in the face of 2 percent to 3 percent inflation. Historically speaking, a strange world, but in reality, was it and is it? Maybe it's the old demand-supply equation that beef producers have adjusted to for a century or more. The gnomes have told us there is too much cash chasing too few investment vehicles, thus the rising demand for stocks (not stockers, unfortunately).

If the gnomes are correct, and who are we to challenge their wisdom, then it will not be long before this phenomenon moves to include rural real estate. In fact, we have seen a dramatic increase in the number of serious inquiries, from capable buyers, for expensive ranch properties. In this regard we would like to offer the following thoughts about purchasing a ranch.

If you are the type individual who looks for a good deal, then you should look for two types of ranches. The first would be an expensive, fully operational, highly developed showplace where the current owners are completely disenchanted and want out, period. The second would probably be at the other end of the spectrum. In all probability it would be poorly developed, with rundown fencing and improvements, pastures that look like the devil's headquarters and the ranch has been leased out for decades. This latter type takes great vision or experience in rejuvenating rural properties, but the financial rewards are usually worth the effort. This is where an experienced land broker or real estate agent can be of valuable assistance, especially one who has been in the area for a long time.

The above are two suggestions we have found to be true about purchasing a ranch. But the principal reason we wanted to write this chapter was to explore what can be done to maximize your investment and make the ranch readily saleable in the event you want to make a change.

And the statistics tell us that most weekend cowboys buy and sell their ranches every three to five years. They are always looking for their perfect place on the range. We do not want to sound like Mr. Nobucks, who has a television program demonstrating how to buy real estate for nothing down and, lo and behold, you turn into an instant multimillionaire. But, through the years, we have learned and practiced, which expenditures and efforts are worthwhile, and which ones you do simply to satisfy yourself or your family.

Money, in most cases, is not the critical ingredient but rather matters such as good taste, orderliness, cleanliness and other factors that contribute to eye appeal. After tending to such chores with a sense of mission, you should promote the property and then it will take on a life of its own. Its reputation should be such that everyone in the county should know your property by name, and what it looks like from the road. You know the type of ranch, the one that everyone longs to own, if only they had enough money. You create an ambiance and reputation that continues to put dollars on the property's value.

Start by putting the property in order and decide to keep it that way. Order must be a state of mind. It is one that creates a feeling of well-being or esteem and above all gives you and your family a sense of pride. As we have alluded to before, there are two objectives a weekend cowboy should meet, one is financial and the other is emotional. Both are important to owning a successful ranch and both contribute to your overall goals and well-being.

Most of the remaining practices are essentially operational.

First, pick up trash, broken limbs and other debris on the ranch. If dead trees exist either cut them down or have a bulldozer push them over. If you have the time, inclination and need, cut the trees into suitable pieces for firewood. Otherwise, solicit a firewood dealer to help you eliminate the remains. In areas where permitted, it is usually most efficient to burn the remaining roots, then spread the ashes. Make sure you are prepared for this task with proper permits, etc. and be sure there is not a moratorium on burning because of extremely dry conditions. Sometimes it may be helpful to have a local volunteer fire department pumper on location in the event a fire gets out of control. The volunteers may incorporate the program into their training exercise. From experience, we know they would appreciate a donation towards the fire and ambulance service in the community.

Second, mow the pastures at least twice a year. It will not only improve the eye appeal of the property, but if the timing is correct, mowing can essentially prevent seed production of annual weeds and progressively weaken perennial ones. In theory, the idea is to clip annual weeds before seed formation and perennial weeds before budding, but for your particular area, ask your county agricultural extension agent or a well-respected local rancher or farmer. You may also inquire as to the benefits of a herbicide application at this juncture. We believe adherence to such a schedule for two to three years will show dramatic results.

Third, if you did not do it in your selection process, take some representative soil samples to determine the pH and level of soil nutrients. Apply lime and/or fertilizer accordingly.

Fourth, make sure fence lines are straight and level and posts perpendicular to the ground. This is particularly important along the road, driveway and headquarters area. In addition, with the use of a trimmer, mow under the fence line. You may also use a nonselective herbicide in place of mechanical means. In any event, it will greatly improve eye appeal and also contribute to the life of the fence. If conservation and/or hunting is one of your objectives, a nice trimmed hedgerow, at least ten to twenty feet wide, would be satisfactory. If you are using board fencing, and plan to paint it white, we suggest you prepare the surface well and apply a good oil-based, white undercoat or primer-type paint. This will last much longer than 98 percent of the white fence paint. And it can be purchased in five-gallon containers, which reduces the unit cost substantially (see Chapter Six on improvements and fencing).

Fifth, if needed, grade your main internal roads and make sure they don't hinder the natural surface drainage of the ranch. Otherwise use culverts. Another helpful suggestion: Design your internal roads so that you have a thirty-foot grass shoulder on both sides. This dramatically improves the eye appeal and improves operating efficiency by allowing utilization of the roadway and shoulders as transfer chutes between pastures.

Believe it or not, if you do the above practices on a regular basis, while the ranch is under your ownership, you will be justly rewarded—emotionally while you own it and financially when you sell it. These practices are relatively inexpensive compared to your overall investment. In the farm and ranch real estate business, we see new owners spend large sums of money for unnecessary barns and other structures. Yet, they often ignore those practices that contribute the most to a profitable and enjoyable venture.

Once you have the above recommendations under control, then you should consider landscaping and painting the existing structures—at least the ones you want to keep. Unless you want complete privacy, you should design and install a nice sign at your entrance. Do it in good taste and embody it into your color scheme and promotional program for the ranch. If you do not have the talent to design a sign, then enlist the aid of an advertising or promotional firm that is experienced in the cattle business. The sign will cost relatively little, but it gives cohesiveness to your program for a long time.

The appearance of the ranch house is really a matter of personal taste. We can tell you from a real estate perspective that, in general, most of the money should be invested into the ranch to make it more efficient and productive, with great eye appeal. This does not preclude having a nice home on the ranch, whether you renovate the existing one, or build a new one. What we are talking about is whether you should build a River Oaks, Beverly Hills, Palm Beach or Greenwich-type home on the ranch. Our experience leads us to believe that such an edifice will substantially reduce the marketability of the property and one rarely recovers the money invested to build it. What little advice we offer along these lines, is that as you develop the ranch, make sure you have a home on the property that you like so that your family can *live* the ranch experience.

Chapter 5

Managing Pastures and Hay Crops

General Considerations

Despite the dramatic changes and technological breakthroughs in science and the beef industry, the importance and relationship between forage and beef cattle remain the same as they have for centuries. As ruminants, beef cattle have a unique ability to get most of their nutrition from roughage. Roughage means, in our limited sense, grasses or legumes in the natural form, as pastures, in the harvested, green form as silage, or the dry form, as hay.

It is this unique character of beef cattle that enables them to convert relatively low-cost roughage into high-value animal protein that we recognize and appreciate as rib roast, T-bone steak, ground beef, etc. Since it is generally recognized that more than 80 percent of the feed consumed by beef cattle is forage, i.e., either grazed or consumed as silage or hay, it follows that the management of pastures will have a large impact on the overall success of the ranching venture. And it does! Therefore, become knowledgeable about forage production in your area. Be sure to go to your county agricultural extension agent, or even to the agricultural college or the experiment station in your state to inquire about and look at demonstration plots. Learn the best varieties or cultivars for your ranch and how to keep them not only in top production, but also high in nutrient value and palatability.

Forage Crops

Most forage species have a wide range of geographic adaptation. However, the varietal form gives it usefulness in a specific location. The variable nature of the climate, and the internal drainage of soils, their pH and their fertility, are major considerations in matching the forage variety with the actual site.

Because of the great geographical diversity of both forage varieties and production practices, it is outside the scope of this book to detail every scenario for every area in the continental United States. However, we will summarize the major geographic areas of the country. Then we will use Area 2—The South, where we currently live, to go through a more detailed syllabus. The minutiae will be different for each area but the principles will be the same.

Before you begin establishing a new pasture, take inventory of the existing situation. In the preceding chapter we advised you to mow or clip the pastures, take soil samples and apply lime or fertilizer as dictated by the soil analysis and the recommendations. See what improvements arise from these cultural practices. In many cases you may not need a new pasture, but merely a renovated one. Be aware that the investment in a new pasture may not necessarily improve your returns or net income. Maybe weed control, either by mowing and/or herbicides, fertilization, proper stocking rates and a grazing system will be adequate for several years. It has been our experience that many ranches, which are for sale, also have been leased for grazing purposes and the majority are overstocked with little or no benefit of a satisfactory grazing system. The consequence is few good grasses, but a lot of weeds.

Now let's discuss the forage crops themselves. While there are many classifications, such as grass versus legume, cool versus warm season, and native versus improved, we have used a geographic classification and have identified the major grass and legume species or mixtures that are adapted and used in each of the seven geographic areas of the country.

Area 1: The Northeast

Timothy, Kentucky bluegrass, orchard grass, alfalfa and varying amounts of wild white clover and other legumes are the major forage species in this area. Unimproved permanent pastures may contain bent grass or poverty grass.

Area 2: The South

This is a large, humid area extending in the north to Virginia and as far west as the coastal plain of Texas. The species of forage plants common to the northern part of this area are Kentucky bluegrass, orchard grass, tall fescue, white clover, red clover and alfalfa. They frequently are found in combinations or mixtures such as orchard grass and ladino clo-

Timothy

ver, tall fescue and ladino clover, orchard grass and alfalfa, and Kentucky bluegrass and white clover. Coastal Bermuda grass dominates the southern portion of this area although there is also use of bahia grass, dallis grass, Johnson grass, white clover, and lespe-

deza. Recently Klein grass 75 has been introduced in the western part of this area. Mixtures of dallis grass and white clover and bahia/white clover are for soils more prone to be wet while Bermuda grass/lespedeza mixtures are used where the soils are deep and well drained. With Coastal Bermuda grass, yields are largely dependent upon ample rainfall or irrigation during the growing season. With sufficient fertility, particularly nitrogen, yields of four to eight tons per acre of dry forage or 400 to 600 pounds of beef per acre can be obtained with the

Kentucky bluegrass

proper soils and management.

Area 3: The Central United States and the Lake States

Alfalfa, either alone or with a grass, is the predominant recommendation for hay production in this area. Grasses used in the mixture are smooth brome grass, timothy, or orchard grass. The most popular grass production in the area is Kentucky bluegrass followed by timothy. However, it is generally thought production would be improved by adding legumes, such as lespedeza, ladino clover, red clover or birdsfoot trefoil.

Area 4: Great Plains

As in the preceding area, alfalfa is the principal legume hay here. Brome grass, wheat grass, bluegrass, and needle grass are also found. They are important because they make most of their growth in early spring and fall. On the other hand, the bluestems,

Alfalfa

switch grass, Indian grass, sideoats grama, blue grama and buffalo grass make most of their growth and are most palatable in the summer, thus, they are essentially used for summer forage. The growth characteristic of the species is important to how it is adapted into the farm or ranch production program.

Orchard grass

Area 5: The Rocky Mountains

The mountains of this area are used only in the summer; valleys are mainly only productive in the winter—unless they are irrigated. Alfalfa is the number one, seeded hay crop; hay from native plants may compete for this position. Alsike clover, red clover, alfalfa, smooth brome grass, intermediate wheat grass, meadow foxtail, orchard grass, reed canary grass, and timothy are satisfactory for use in improved pastures or meadows.

Alsike clover

Area 6: The Southwest

This area includes all the western and most of the northern part of Texas, parts of Oklahoma, Kansas, and the southeast corner of Colorado and essentially all of Arizona and New Mexico. It is a large area, composed for our purposes of irrigated land and what we, in South Texas, call range land. By and large, the limited amount of rainfall is a characteristic of the area. This coupled with the prevailing soil types and their fertility requires that the land be irrigated to be highly productive. There are some exceptions in the eastern section, where small grains such as wheat, oats, barley and ryegrass are grown. In fact, small grain or ryegrass pastures are important on some farms and ranches in the area. On the irrigated lands, however, alfalfa is still the number one forage but Coastal Ber-

Bermuda grass

muda grass, tall fescue, blue panic grass, tall wheat grass, and intermediate wheat grass also make an important contribution to both pastures and hay production. Brush control, followed by the seeding of native species, such as bluestem, switch grass, and Indian grass are essential with pure rangeland.

Area 7: The Pacific Coast

In this area, alfalfa is the number one hay crop because of its high yields, high quality, excellent market demand and its role in crop rotation. For pastures, alfalfa is combined with one of the grasses such as orchard grass, tall fescue or one of the wheat grasses. In the southern portion of the area, and in desert valleys, Coastal Bermuda grass takes a predominant position. This is a large geographic area with many different climates, so be sure to check this one out thoroughly. What may do well in one small area may be a total disaster in another.

Tall fescue

New Pastures

Now to discuss the remaining principles of a pasture and hay program we will use, as an example, the western portion of Area 2—The South. The forage system with which we are most familiar, and which provides a high degree of production potential is: 1) a well-managed program of Coastal Bermuda grass, both for grazing and hay, and 2) a so-called cool season annual small grain, ryegrass or legume planting, either alone or over the coastal sod. If in Texas, ask your Extension Forage Specialist at Texas A & M, or the Rice-Pasture Extension Center in Beaumont, for the latest in varietal recommendations. Otherwise, inquire at the state university where your ranch is located. There are many excellent cultivars that have substantially improved the nutritional value and palatability of forage species. With respect to your own operations, we encourage you to be inquisitive and analytical, write down everything you do with specific dates, climatic conditions prevailing at the time, so you can understand the results of your program and thus become an informed and successful weekend cowboy.

If you have decided that a new Coastal Bermuda grass pasture is warranted, the first three things you need to do are:

1) select the proper cultivar of Coastal Bermuda grass and arrange, at an early date, for its purchase;

2) study the soil analysis report for the need, and recommendations for lime and/or fertilizer and

3) prepare the seedbeds or in this case, sprig-bed.

The importance of seedbed preparation cannot be overemphasized. Make sure adequate lime and phosphorus are added prior to or at sprigging, if your soils are strongly acidic and low in available phosphorus. Remember Coastal is a strongly nitrogen-dependent and responsive forage. However, nitrogen should not be added prior to, or at, planting if weeds are a problem. Either use an herbicide, where the nitrogen can be applied at sprigging, or delay the application of nitrogen until the sprigs are established and better able to compete with the weeds. If weeds are not a problem, you have the option. It is thought best to apply the fertilizer two to four inches below the sprigs. The sprigs are planted in late winter or spring at the rate of eighteen to twenty bushels per acre. Ensure that the sprigs are fresh, weed-free, shaded and moist from digging until planting. With adequate moisture the sprigs will spread rapidly and need additional nitrogen. If hay is to be obtained in the first year forty to one hundred pounds of nitrogen per acre may be needed in addition to the amount applied at sprigging. Moisture, however, will be your limiting factor.

Fertilization

To realize the full potential of Coastal Bermuda grass a good production and management program must be carried out. This is true for essentially all the so-called improved grasses. But since fertilizer costs represent such a significant portion of the preharvest cost of pasture or hay, there is a tendency to reduce or eliminate fertilizer in the program. However, do not succumb to this temptation. While we agree that the relationship between nutrient cost and cattle prices makes this decision apparently difficult at times, there are other factors involved. Reducing fertilizer, especially on Coastal Bermuda grass pastures, reduces yields, the longevity of the stand, and forage quality while encouraging the invasion of weeds. Furthermore, a reduction will not reduce fixed costs, such as taxes, interest, depreciation on equipment and cow herd, but will contribute to a degradation in eye appeal. Most improved cultivars were selected because of improvements in yield, due to their response to fertilization, mainly nitrogen. The amount of fertilizer needed per acre depends on the fertility of the soil, the desired production level (tons per acre or the stocking rate) and whether the pastures will be used for grazing, hay or both.

Generally in our area of Texas, if lime, phosphorus and potassium are needed, they are applied at one time in the spring. The nitrogen may be applied in split applications of fifty pounds of actual nitrogen per acre several times during the grazing cycle or after each hay cutting. The fertilizer-response curve with Coastal Bermuda grass shows that you need approximately fifty pounds of actual nitrogen for every ton of hay or equivalent production. Therefore, if you plan harvesting approximately six large bales of Coastal per acre you will need to apply at least two hundred to three hundred pounds of nitrogen per acre. With an improved fertilization program, the quality of Coastal improves as nitrogen increases the protein content of the grass. However, proper maturity at harvest is also very important. Beef cattle should graze when the Coastal is young and tender, and hay should be cut at three- to- four-weeks growth to obtain the optimum nutrition per acre. There is only one caveat in this program—do not apply nitrogen too early in the spring because the night temperature must be consistently above 60 degrees Fahrenheit for Coastal Bermuda grass to make efficient utilization of the nitrogen.

Weed Control

With respect to weed control, the first thing you should do is identify the various weed species present. Experience the fun of being a plant taxonomist. Seriously though, you should learn to identify the major weeds you may encounter in your area. Again, your agricultural extension agent will probably direct you to pamphlets and keys that will assist you in this challenge. In most cases, mowing at the proper time will give reasonably good control, but if you have your pasture in a highly productive mode you may also want to use a herbicide. Check with your local farm supply store or extension personnel for the approved chemicals, and always follow the label directions and use at recommended rates.

Stocking Rates

The remaining issues mostly involve stocking rates, pasture size and grazing systems. The advice of experienced and qualified pasture specialists is extremely helpful in determining the carrying capacity of the pasture. Available forage is related primarily to growing conditions (mainly rainfall and fertility), characteristics such as size, sex, and age of the individual animal, and the grazing system employed. It is important not to undergraze because the grass becomes less nutritious and unpalatable while overgrazing weakens the plants, reduces the yield and encourages weed invasion. A system, whereby the grazing on a given pasture, on which each rotation is completed in no longer than a week and does not reduce the grass below two to three inches, seems to be consistent with economy and a good pasture-animal balance. However, if wildlife, such as deer and quail, are important to you, then critical management of livestock stocking rates must be considered, because grazing does influence wildlife habitat.

To Bale or Not to Bale

A bale of hay, whether in the form of rectangular bales or large circular ones weighing as much as a ton each, is probably the most recognizable symbol of rural real estate. To illustrate the importance of hay in cattle production, it is generally recognized that domestically, more than 150 million tons of hay are produced from over 60 million acres.

For hay to be nutritionally useful, the crop must be of high quality, cut at the optimum stage of maturity for maximum nutrient yield without harmful damage to future cuttings, and cured properly so that the moisture content is reduced to approximately 18 percent.

The time and money spent to grow and harvest these crops are very significant to the beef cattle operation and should be proportionate to the need for hay versus the price and availability of other sources of roughage, such as winter annuals, and, of course, the value of the livestock.

It is, therefore, important to consider the cost-return relationship with respect to the question of to bale or not to bale.

For this discussion let us return to the real-life example we used in Chapter Three. This ranch has excellent Coastal pastures and the production potential is such that 900 acres could be used for hay cutting. The three options available to the operators of the ranch are:

1) cut forage and bale the hay yourself,
2) have a custom operator harvest the hay, or
3) buy hay and put the cattle on pastures.

Fortunately, this ranch has excellent cost accounting and an analysis was done to help answer this question. In order to provide uniformity in analysis, a base of 6,000 x 1,500 pound round bales of hay was used as the standard for all three options. (See figure 6)

The result of this analysis is: if cost were the only consideration, you would bale the hay yourself or possibly have it harvested on a custom basis. In order to harvest top quality, palatable hay, it must be cut on a critical-time or growth-stage basis. Thus you may be at the whim of the custom operator.

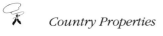

Option 1—Cut and Bale Yourself (1999)

Production Costs	$/Per Acre	Total	
Potash, 150 lbs./acre	9.00	$8,100	
Spreading	2.75	2,475	
Liquid Fertilizer	34.25	30,825	
1st Application	2.75	2,475	
Liquid Fertilizer	34.35	30,908	
2nd Application	2.75	2,475	
Herbicide	6.00	5,400	
Total Production Cost			$82,658

Machinery Repair Cost + Fuel & Twine

Hay Machinery Repairs			
Tractors	$6,448		
Balers	3,344		
Mowers	2,808		
Rakes	500		
		$13,100	
Fuel		8,277	
Bale Twine		3,700	
Total Repairs, Fuel, & Twine Cost			$25,077

Machinery Cost

Cutting			
JD 2950 Tractor	$5,955		
NH 463 Mower	6,000		
		$11,955	
Raking			
JD 2550 Tractor	1,299		
Hay Rake	1,740		
		3,039	
Baling			
JD 4050 Tractor	2,164		
JD 535 Baler	3,900		
		6,064	
Total Machinery Cost			$21,058

Labor Cost

Employee 1	3,840		
Employee 2	3,600		
Employee 3	7,560		
Other	1,800		
Total Labor Cost		$16,800	

Total Cost to Cut & Bale			$145,593

Option 2—Custom Harvest Cost (1999)

6,000 bales x $15.00/bale	$90,000	
Fertilizer & Herbicide	82,658	
Less savings on labor	(15,000)	
Total Custom Harvest Cost		$157,658

Option 3—Purchase Hay (1999)

6,000 bales x $30/bale	$180,000	
Fertilizer for pastures only	39,937	
Less savings on labor	(15,000)	
Total Cost of Purchase		$204,937

	Cost per 1,500 lb. bale
Option 1 — Cut and Bale Yourself	$24.27
Option 2 — Custom Harvest	$26.28
Option 3 — Purchase Hay	$34.16

Figure 6. A comparison of cost for various hay-procurement options.

What ever practice or system employed, the goal is to obtain high-quality hay at a reasonably competitive cost. Consequently, after analyzing the three options, the management of this ranch decided to cut and bale the hay themselves.

Annual winter/spring pastures

To conclude this chapter, we would like to discuss the use of winter annuals as a forage crop in the Texas Gulf Coast of Area 2—The South. When used properly, and with a little help from the weather, small grains and ryegrass can provide a tremendous amount of inexpensive nutrients for grazing animals.

Growth response to temperature is the single most important factor in selecting a winter annual species. Of the grazing crops adapted to Texas conditions, ryegrass grows at the lowest temperature; hence, we have used ryegrass both alone and over Coastal Bermuda grass sod, with excellent results. Since in the humid south rust is usually a problem in winter-type grazing, make sure you use a rust-resistant variety such as Gulf. It is usually seeded at the rate of fifteen to twenty pounds per acre in September or early October. The forage is always high quality, until the seed head forms. A

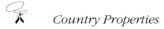

practical reminder: The period of greatest growth is early spring, therefore, in a cow/calf operation it may be exploited better in a fall calving program rather than a spring one. As with Coastal Bermuda grass, ryegrass responds well to nitrogen fertilization.

Chapter 6

Some Thoughts on Fencing and Improvements

We are real fussbudgets when it comes to fencing—many have said it reflects our personalities. In any event, a good fence is not only a necessity in today's cattle business, but it also adds substantially to the eye appeal of the property and ultimately to its value. To have a good fence, you need the commitment and dedication of the fence builder and owner. Pride in craft and ownership are two qualities we believe are helpful, but lacking these, you must rely on "doing it the right way."

Construction Suggestions

Most good fence construction has shown the test of time. It will be straight and follow the contours of the land in a rolling smooth fashion. The posts should be perpendicular to the ground line and be set at least three and one-half feet deep in the soil. If you select a ranch where the fencing appears to be in good shape, maybe all you will need to do is clean up the fence row, rebrace the corners and pull posts, and repair the actual fence. You can obtain helpful hints and suggestions from the Agricultural Engineering Department of your state agricultural college or handbooks, which you will find in their library.

If you are going to build a new fence make sure the posts are at least eight feet long so that the buried portion can be three and one-half feet, leaving fifty-four inches for the above-ground portion. For line posts, use a diameter of six inches if wood or five inches for pipe, while the corner posts and pull posts should be at least six to eight inches. We recommend using hardwood. But if you must use softwood, make sure the posts are properly pressure treated with a biocide before installation. It is preferable to use a double-span system (see figure 7) for wooden corner and gate posts, rather than the single-span anchor arrangement. Metal line posts are also popular and may be interspersed with wooden posts for greater stability. Such a system also provides a degree of protection as it can act as a grounding device in the event of an electrical storm.

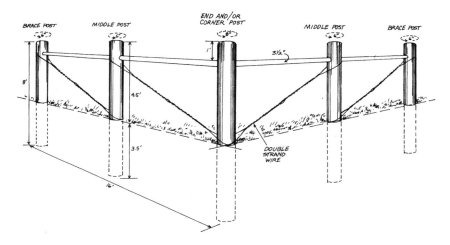

Fig. 7. Diagram of a double-span corner system for wood fence and gate posts.

Optimum post spacing depends on the cattle density, but in general a spacing of sixteen feet is adequate for a barbed wire fence. Wooden fences require an eight-foot spacing, while a ten- to twelve-foot interval is usually satisfactory for woven wire fences.

Curved fences pose other problems that create stress lines so that the posts are pulled in and the fence becomes unstable and unsightly. A good friend, who recently built a new fence along the road, used the center line of the road as his base line. He built the fence along the curve in the road, shortened the interval between posts and kept only light tension on the barbed wire. So far, it looks great.

The two most common fencing materials used in beef cattle production are barbed wire and woven wire. Wire size is stated by gauge, the larger the number, the smaller the gauge. Most common are 12.5- and 13.5-gauge, however, a high tensile-strength wire up to 18-gauge is now available. Make sure the wire has a thick coat of rust-resistant zinc on the outside; this determines its rust-free life. If your fence is barbed wire, use four or five strands of two- or four-point wire. If woven wire is used, put one or two strands of barbed wire on the top to stop cattle from reaching over and pressing down on the fence. When you attach the wire to the post, do not drive the staple completely into the post. You need to give the wire some leeway for expansion and contraction. This will permit good tension without damaging the integrity of the post-soil geometry. As a finishing touch you may want to sight, through a transom, the tops of the posts and cut them off with a chain saw so the flow of the fence looks smooth.

If you go to the expense of a wooden board and painted fence, use brass or at least galvanized screws for attachment of the seasoned boards to the posts. For the line fence use four boards of 1 x 6- or 8- inch treated wood and after an additional six months of seasoning, paint it with a high quality outside oil-based undercoat or primer. If you use a double coat, it may be satisfactory for many years. At least it will not peel or flake as most cheap white paint the farm store may suggest you buy. We have found this out ourselves and we can attest that you will be much happier. You may also be pleased with the use of a low-voltage electric wire on the top and pasture-side of the wooden fence to keep cattle and horses from leaning against it.

Remember, the fence is a long-term investment, maybe twenty-five years or more, so construct it right with good materials. You will not only save labor costs, you will save yourself the emotional distress of watching a poorly constructed fence deteriorate. We are not talking about spending a lot more money but solely maintaining the dedication and discipline to do it right.

Gates or Gaps

We have strong feelings about the fascinating subject of gates or gaps in the fence. A lot of ingenuity has been employed to solve the simple objectives of retaining cattle while permitting the entry of man with his vehicle. There have been many types of gaps invented or devised from the simple "cattle guard" consisting of a series of parallel metal rods two to four inches apart that fit into the roadway, to the bump-type gates developed and used by the King Ranch in South Texas.

We'd like to share a recent cute and humorous true story. Our newly hired accountant—a recent graduate of a prestigious Ivy League institution—called to say that an official tax investigator was in her office checking current employment records. And they found a major problem. They could not find any employment records for the cattle guards. Apparently, in all sincerity, both of these conscientious, serious and ambitious new employees thought cattle guards were employees guarding cattle. Or maybe, they were just pulling our legs a little. I know we had a good laugh.

Back to fencing: First, use a gap opening of at least sixteen feet. Many people mistakenly build a fence with too narrow a gap. The end result is that the gate or post is clobbered by machinery and vehicles. Second, use the heavy galvanized iron gates that you see in the major livestock shows and in your ranch supply store. They are usually painted green, blue, red and or silver/aluminum. Do not use the extruded ones—they are flimsy and can be easily ripped out of your hand by the wind. And third, secure the gate to a post that is deeply anchored and well-braced in the ground, with anchor plates and well-set cement (seven days). And finally, install a support block under the free end of the gate to prevent the effects of leverage, such as sagging.

Corrals, Barns and Handling Equipment

The best advice we can give about corrals, and handling equipment such as working chutes, loading chutes, squeeze chutes, head clamps, tilting tables, is go to your Agricultural Extension Service office and obtain their recommendations and plans for your area. Your own personal preference and those of your help, should play a role in the final design. Be sure to place the corrals in a well-drained area where the soil type encourages firm footing for cattle and man. No gumbo-type soils, please! If this is not practical, build up the area with road-type materials, but be sure to provide proper drainage.

In Chapter One we talked about the value of cattle barns. We also suggest that a storage barn for high-value feeds, tools, and equipment would be very useful. In addition, we recommend that you have a quarantine area for new cattle, and for sick ones from your current herd. In the latter case, be sure to consider surface-drainage patterns and prevailing winds. Also, make sure the water system is a nonsiphoning type, either by system selection or by the use of a check valve.

Chapter 7

Managing the Beef Cattle Herd

General Thoughts

Good fencing and gates are only part of your cattle management program. We assume that you have selected your type of cattle operation and the breed. But before you commit money to purchase the cows and calves, give considerable thought to the preoperating plan. Do you know the advantages and disadvantages of a commercial cow/calf operation, and likewise for a purebred and registered herd? Do you have the financial resources, the time and personality traits to be successful in this challenging business? If there is any advice we can give to first-time ranchers/breeders that will really make a difference, it is to thoroughly study and evaluate the first stages of your new venture. The breeding business, by nature, is a long-term commitment and investment. Consequently, many of the decisions you make in the beginning will have important long-term influences.

Be sure you are happy with the breed, regardless of the technical evaluation. If you aren't excited about the selection, then the odds are that you will ultimately lose interest in the beef-cattle industry. Take time and, if needed, get some technical advice on the selection of your foundation herd. Try to avoid extremes but emphasize predictable performance in the desirable traits with the proper use of EPDs. Again, this important early decision will affect a good part of the life span of the ranch, whether visually on the ranch or genetically in your future herd. Remember the old saying, "Haste makes waste."

Be confident of your decision and buy only the best breeding stock or the top of the line. If you are new in the business your reputation will be based on the type of cattle you buy. Therefore, don't be enticed for any reason to buy second-class cattle. We know some people will disagree with this philosophy as they put an economic factor into their decision, but take it from us, buy the best and in the long run you will be far better off. This is true for most any long-term investment, certainly true for antiques and precious stones and we know it is more so for any investment that eats. We learned this the hard and expensive way when we were heavily involved in the horse business. Don't waste your feed and management talent on the "has-beens" or "no-gooders."

One other point we learned that may be helpful—there always will be good cattle available to purchase. A new entrant into the business may become impatient with the progress of his acquisition program and may want to lower his standards or increase his bids to unreasonable levels. Don't despair, there will be good cattle at another sale on another day. With over 100 million cattle in the United States today no one can corner or cause significant ripples in this huge market.

Ways to Establish a Herd

There are several ways to establish your cow/calf herd but the most popular and logical are: 1) Purchase a complete herd that has an excellent reputation. This will give you instant notoriety in the industry and your breed association; 2) Buy cow/calf combinations at sales and private treaty; and 3) Buy yearling heifers only—50 percent more than your anticipated herd size and cull 50 percent the first year. Then cull the bottom 25 percent the following year so that future calves will be considerably better and worth more than previous ones.

Selection Criteria

In selecting your individual animals, the criteria listed below should be the basis for the selection process, but we hope you now know what a good cow and calf should look like. If not, be sure to visit some good cattle operations, production sales, and also go to the library at your State Agricultural College and look at books on stock judging, beef cattle, or the beef industry.

Appearance: The important prerequisites for a good beef type are size, breed type, sex characteristics, and conformation, including structural soundness. They all contribute to the overall impression of the animal and some of these traits are moderately to highly heritable. Remember, even with all the attention given to EPDs appearance is important in the real world. In the commercial market it is usually the only criteria a feeder buyer uses for his selection and price.

Fig. 7. The ideal cow

Pedigree: The pedigree, per se, isn't nearly as important now that all the performance and progeny records are readily available. However, for newer cow families and to search for rare or obscured genetic defects, such as dwarfism, you should make a thorough check of the pedigree. It is also important to make new investments in animals which exhibit the current thinking for type, size, conformation, etc. Also, you should reflect about the future and where it is taking the breed. The importance of a popular family is exemplified when future price levels bring joy to the rancher. Thus, a consideration of the pedigree remains important.

Performance Records: Birth weights, weaning weights, weaning conformation scores, yearly weights, yearly conformation scores, and ratios for all prospects compared to parents or half siblings are very useful. Select your animals only from known herds with good performance records. Always buy the "cream of the crop."

Freedom from Disease: While this sounds like a logical and obvious criterion, sometimes new purchases slip through the analytical net. That's why it is good to have a quarantine area on the ranch and to place new additions there before adding them to the herd. Many a top, careful breeder has been fooled because of a masked carrier of a disease, such as with a vaccinated calf that tests positive for Brucellosis and yet is sold as Brucellosis-free.

Age: Usually, younger is better.

Climatic Adaptation: This probably was thought out in the preselection process, but if you are involved in crossbreeding, it will come up again. Cattle with Brahman blood in crosses with British or continental breeds tend to provide a degree of tolerance to high temperatures and humidity values because of their ability to perspire and modulate their body temperature. For this and other reasons, it is believed Brahman-blood cattle are more resistant to many of the tropical parasites, diseases and insects.

Ease of Calving: Ease of calving is a very important trait, especially when selecting for large, growthy heifers. Cows with large pelvic openings, and heifers with lower birth weights contribute to ease of calving. But, in the end, rely on a sire with good expected progeny differences (EPDs) for lower birth weights and unassisted births.

In selecting the sire, you make an important decision that will strongly impact the herd. In fact, it is the most important and long-lasting decision you will make relative to a herd's reputation and merit. The sire  and dam essentially contribute equally to the inheritance of the offspring, but because the bull services more females, his impact on the herd is greater. In a purebred or registered herd, the use of ova transplant and artificial insemination (A.I.) may be practical and thereby you have the option to limit the sire's influence on the overall herd.

Artificial Insemination versus the Natural Way

Cows normally come into heat or estrus every twenty-one days for a period of approximately fifteen hours; successful breeding must take place during this time period. Gestation—the period from breeding to birth—is approximately nine months. For this discussion we should mention both natural and A.I. service. A.I. costs compare favorably with natural service. While the cost per calf is slightly higher with A.I., the benefits of higher weaning weights, a more uniform calf crop and better animal health bring the equation into balance. Both methods should provide the same end product and the criteria used to select the sire are the same. But with natural service, you normally buy the bull from the breeder, after visual inspection of not only the prospect, but his immediate relatives. In your selection process, in addition to studying the bull's conformation and soundness, do not use a bull or its service unless there are good production and complete progeny records available for your inspection and use. Most all traits you look for in beef cattle, with the exception of fertility, are moderate to highly heritable, as shown below. Most, with the exception of birth weight, have economic importance. Some carcass traits, like rib eye area, have a heritability estimate of 70 percent. Therefore, use bulls and semen that have good EPD values. By using this system, you can select sires that produce progeny with consistent predictability for the traits that are important in your individual breeding program.

Traits in Beef Cattle

Highly Heritable	*Moderately Heritable*
Color	Birth weight
Carcass	Carcass
Fat thickness	Quality grade
Rib eye area	Yield grade
Tenderness	Conformation
Polledness	Feed efficiency
Postweaning gain	Weaning weight

Finally, in the selection of a sire, check for any undesirable hereditary defects. There are about 200 inherited abnormalities in cattle. If there is a history of any heritable defect in the pedigree use another sire. We are confident this should not be a problem because of the quality of sires listed with the large semen service companies or with longtime respected purebred breeders, but it is worth mentioning.

Genetics for the Layman

General: We do not want to get into highly detailed breeding programs, but will refer you to the many excellent texts on the subject. Instead, we would like to discuss some basic principles of heredity and in layman's language explain how they influence some economically important and intellectually interesting traits in beef cattle. The questions children often ask are, "Why does one cow have horns and the other doesn't?" or "Why are all the cows and calves in that field black?"

Both of these obvious traits are the result of a very complicated sounding term: Mendel's Laws of Inheritance. But in actual practice the laws are quite simple, and, in fact, the inheritance for both these traits is called simple inheritance. The basic answer to the two questions above is that they are inherited from their parents. But how? The kids will not let you get away that easily. The answers lie in tiny microscopic particles in the nuclei of the cells called genes. DNA, is the chemical structure of the gene and provides a blueprint for development and function, such as horns and color. Genes are the basic unit of heredity; they occur in pairs at specific locations on the chromosome, but are transmitted by the parents singly to the offspring.

Chromosomes are the long protein-like molecules on which the genes are located. In beef cattle, there are thirty pairs of chromosomes or a total of sixty chromosomes. One member of each pair is inherited from the male parent while the other member of that pair is inherited from the female parent. Inasmuch as genes are carried on chromosomes, everything that happens to chromosomes also happens to genes. Thus, at random, one member of each gene pair comes from the male while the other member of that gene pair comes from the maternal or female side. Each calf starts life as a single fertilized egg. The egg rapidly divides to create two, four, eight, sixteen, ... cells. And remember, as a cell divides, it is necessary to make a copy of all the DNA in the cell. When the division process is completed, each offspring has two complete copies of all the DNA needed for life. In turn, this individual mating will pass on half its genetic inheritance to its progeny.

Polled vs. Horned Cattle: Getting back to the horned question, we say that polledness is simple inheritance or governed by one gene we call large "**P**" where large "**P**" is dominant over little "p." The opposite condition with horns we will call recessive or little "p." Remember the genes are in pairs thus we have three possible combinations influencing the polled trait. They are "**PP**," "**Pp**," and "pp" and half of each pair is inherited from each parent. If we breed polled to horned as follows:

	P	P
p	**P**p Polled	**P**p Polled
p	**P**p Polled	**P**p Polled

Horned Dam=pp

Polled Sire=**PP**

All of the offspring of this mating will be polled because "**P**" is dominant over "p." This "**P**p," technically, is called heterozygous polled and because the individual has two different genes it will not breed true for the polled trait.

But to confuse the issue a little, if we breed another polled bull to a horned cow as follows:

The offspring in this example are 50 percent heterozygous polled and 50 percent horned. The "pp" condition with two identical genes is called homozygous and in this case is horned and will always pass the "p" gene because it is all it has.

	P	p
p	**P**p Polled	pp Horned
p	**P**p Polled	pp Horned

Horned Dam=pp   Polled Sire=**P**p

This is like clockwork—maybe that's why they call these things Mendel's Laws. Therefore, we should follow the script to the end and breed a heterozygous polled cow to a heterozygous polled bull.

	P	p
P	**PP** Polled	**P**p Polled
p	**P**p Polled	pp Horned

Polled Dam=**P**p   Polled Sire=**P**p

This mating produces offspring that are 75 percent polled and 25 percent horned. But recognize that in the polled calves approximately one-third will be homozygous for the polled trait. Unfortunately, we can't tell which ones by looking at them.

We can however take this one step further. We can take the males from this mating, wait for sexual maturity, then selectively breed them to a large number of horned cows. If the results of this breeding produce any horned calves, then the male offspring responsible for the mating is heterozygous for the polled trait—remember a homozygous polled bull will always produce polled calves. This is why some people refer to homozygous "**PP**" polled bulls as 100 percent dehorners. With the polled heifer calves at sexual maturity, we send them to an ova transplant center, cross them to a horned bull, transfer the embryos to fourteen or more recipient cows and wait through the 283-day gestation period for the births. If any horned calves are produced, then the donor heifer is heterozygous polled, while if all the fourteen or more offspring are polled, she is almost certainly homozygous for the polled trait.

The wrap up then would be when a homozygous polled bull, "**PP**," meets a homozygous polled gal, "**PP**"—all their offspring will be "**PP**" or homozygously polled.

	P	P
P	**PP** Polled	**PP** Polled
P	**PP** Polled	**PP** Polled

Polled Dam=**PP**   Polled Sire=**PP**

In summary, we have eight possible scenarios with respect to breeding for the polled condition.

1. Homozygous polled sire (**PP**) x homozygous polled dam, (**PP**). All calves will be 100 percent homozygous polled.

2. Homozygous polled sire (**PP**) x horned dam (pp). Calves will be 100 percent heterozygous polled (**P**p).

3. Homozygous polled sire (**PP**) x heterozygous polled dam (**P**p). Calves will be 50 percent homozygous polled (**PP**) and 50 percent heterozygous polled (**P**p).

4. Heterozygous polled sire (**P**p) x heterozygous polled dam (**P**p). Calves will be 25 percent homozygous polled (**PP**), 50 percent heterozygous polled (**P**p), and 25 percent horned (pp).

5. Heterozygous polled sire (**P**p) x horned dam (pp). Calves will be 50 percent horned (pp) and 50 percent heterozygous polled (**P**p).

6. Heterozygous polled sire (**P**p) x homozygous polled dam (**PP**). Calves will be 50 percent homozygous polled (**PP**) and 50 percent heterozygous polled (**P**p).

7. Horned sire (pp) x homozygous polled dam (**PP**). Calves will be 100 percent heterozygous polled (**P**p).

8. Horned sire (pp) x heterozygous polled dam (**P**p). Calves will be 50 percent heterozygous polled (**P**p) and 50 percent horned (pp).

Solely for completeness, may we interject that the above inheritance mechanisms are for the British and North European breeds of beef cattle. If any Zebu blood is in the ancestry, this simple mechanism does not apply as an additional gene (A^f) affects the inheritance in Zebu-type cattle.

Inheritance of Color: Well, what about those black cows and calves? First, they are probably Angus or have Angus in their pedigree somewhere. This very noticeable characteristic is also influenced by just one gene pair. The color black is a dominant trait, "**B**," versus "b" for the recessive gene which when "bb," or double recessive, is red in Angus-type cattle. Most Angus carry double "**BB**" and thus are homozygous for the black color but some may have a "**B**b" heterozygous gene pair. However, these cattle are not apparent by observation due to the dominant black trait gene. If the "**B**bs" are mated together there will be some "bb" or red animals. In fact, the selection for this double- recessive gene has been the basis for a new breed of cattle, namely Red Angus. They have all the other traits of Angus but the normal color. Since each red parent only has "bb," it can't contribute any dominant genes or "**B**'s," so all the offspring from a "bb" x "bb" cross always will be "bb" or red. Conversely, a homozygous black bull (**BB**) crossed with almost any European breed will be all black or have a black body, at least.

When a homozygous Angus is crossed with a homozygous Hereford, you get a white-faced, polled, black-body type offspring. This is because polledness, black color and white face on Hereford are dominant traits. An interesting sidelight to this mating is that many of the white-faced, black, polled calves you see on ranches and in the commercial auctions are the result of Angus and Hereford com-

bining their genetic material so that the dominant genes prevail expressed as polled, black-bodied and white-faced offspring.

We hope the preceding discussion explains some simple inheritance characteristics for beef cattle. Many of the economically important traits, such as carcass traits and rate of gain, are influenced by several gene pairs. Thus, the selection process becomes more complicated. That is why the experts advise against breeding for too many traits at one time. The actual number of genetic combinations becomes overwhelming and it becomes very difficult to analyze the results correctly. However, for our simple inheritance example to get a polled black calf, use a homozygous polled black bull, "**PPBB**," and all the offspring in this F_1 generation will be polled and black.

Hybrid Vigor: Before we leave this section on genes, inheritance and the like, we should briefly mention crossbreeding and hybrid vigor as it relates to your type of cow/calf operation.

The primary goal of crossbreeding (except to dehorn), is hybrid vigor or the tendency of the offspring to be better in certain traits than their parents. Such offspring may be more vigorous, prolific and able to gain weight faster. Commercial operators harness this phenomenon by developing a crossbreeding program to sell F_1 offspring either as heifer replacements or to the feedlot as background feeders. They believe that the progeny will show less mortality and a faster and more efficient rate of growth. In our area, this type of crossbreeding cow/calf program has been very successful. In fact, many producers have gained their reputation in the industry for having good F_1 sales of crossbred cattle.

The Health of the Herd

General: One of the most important aspects of your management program will be your attention to the health of the herd. This program will have a major influence on your bottom line. Not only are the cost of medicines and vaccinations significant, but failure to use them appropriately, will result in higher mortality rates, lower rates of gain and low conception rates. Additionally, it may become difficult to sell your cattle.

Therefore, one of the first things you should do when you acquire the ranch and plan your operating program is to inquire about a well-established large-animal veterinarian in your area and make an appointment for a visit. Talk to him about designing a herd health program for your particular operation. Even if you are a completely new weekend cowboy, he will usually be pleased to help you get off on the right foot because the core of a herd-health program is essentially preventive in nature. If you develop a good relationship, he will be a valuable source of information on the technicalities of your breeding program, insect and parasite problems, and other day-to-day concerns. In cattle country, you will probably need a good veterinarian more than you need an M.D. In any event, even if you have an excellent veterinarian, make sure that you are familiar with the diseases that affect beef cattle in your area. Know the signs and symptoms of disease and parasite infection. It will make you a more confident and informed rancher. Most of the diseases listed below can be controlled by vaccines, antibiotics, control of vectors and a good sanitation program. An effective vaccination program raises the level of resistance to pathogens before disease develops, and helps reduce medicine costs and death losses. Ultimately, the program will enhance the efficiency and reputation of your herd. However, stay current on new problems in your area and the means of control or prevention.

Common Diseases of Beef Cattle

While we list the most common diseases of beef cattle in the United States, we do not want you to become unduly alarmed. Each specific disease is serious if found in the herd, however, the overall incidence is considered low. The descriptions are not meant to be intimidating, but, are included to make you aware of them so you can take proper preventive or remedial action.

Anaplasmosis: An infectious disease caused by a minute parasite that invades the red blood cells. It is spread by biting insects. Symptoms include severe anemia in mature animals accompanied by difficult breathing, pounding heart and yellow mucous membranes. The recommended control methods are vaccination, with two doses of vaccine administered six weeks apart and spraying for insects that spread the disease.

Blackleg: An acute infectious disease caused by an anaerobic bacterium, *Clostridium*. Symptoms include high fever and swelling of the muscles, especially in the shoulders and legs. Vaccinate at three to four months of age, as a preventive measure.

Bovine Virus Diarrhea: A virus disease characterized by high fever, nasal discharge, rapid breathing, loss of appetite and in some cases diarrhea. Vaccinate for prevention.

Brucellosis or Bang's Disease: This is one of the most important and serious diseases affecting beef cattle. It is caused by one of three strains of the bacterium *Brucella*, and in cattle is characterized by abortion, retained afterbirth, uterine infections, and the necessity for several services per conception. Fortunately, in the United States, the federal-state control eradication program has been successful in reducing the incidence of the disease. This program mainly involves blood testing and certifying Brucellosis-free herds and areas. All female beef cattle should be vaccinated between four and twelve months.

Calf Diphtheria: An acute infectious bacterial (*Fusobacterium necrophorum*) disease. The symptoms are manifested as difficulty in breathing, eating and drinking. Vaccinate for prevention.

Hemorrhagic Fever or Shipping Fever: An interesting disease that is thought to be caused by a group of bacteria and viruses. It usually occurs when cattle are under stress, such as during shipping—hence the name Shipping Fever. Actually, other stress situations, such as weaning, lack of rest, and a change in weather or feed, can contribute to the onset of this disease. Symptoms include stressed breathing, unusually high temperature, discharge from the eye and nose and a hacking cough. Vaccination is suggested before the stress period.

Infectious Bovine Rhinotracheitis or Red Nose: A virus disease of the upper respiratory tract, where the symptoms may be confused with Shipping Fever. Additionally, it may also cause inflammation of the vagina and abortion in some animals. Vaccinate for prevention.

Malignant Edema: This is an acute, infectious, usually fatal, toxemia-type disease caused by *Clostridium septicum* and an open wound. The affected animal breathes rapidly, goes off feed, and has gangrene at the site of an open wound on the leg. A gaseous and malodorous fluid exudes from the wound, hence, the common name of gas gangrene. In advanced stages of the disease the animal is most often disoriented. This disease can be mistaken for Blackleg. Vaccinate for prevention when the calves are three to four months of age.

Pinkeye: An infectious eye ailment caused by several bacteria and/or viruses and thought to be encouraged by vitamin A deficiency, dust, insects and intense sunlight. The bacterial form manifests itself in cattle as redness and swelling of the membrane of the eye with liberal tearing and a tendency for the affected animal to keep the eye closed. There may be pus and ulcers of the cornea and blindness may follow in some cases. In the viral form, the disease mainly affects only the eyelids and the tissues surrounding the eyes. Prevention is by good sanitation, controlling face flies, good nutrition and vaccination before the onset of signs and symptoms (pregnant cows should not be vaccinated).

Vibriosis: A bacterial disease caused by *Vibrio fetus* which manifests itself in a beef herd through low fertility rates, an extended breeding period, and abortions in the middle third of pregnancy. Vaccinate before breeding for prevention.

Insects and Parasites of Beef Cattle

The most troublesome insects and parasites on beef cattle in the United States are:

Flies	Liver flukes	Grubs
Lung worms	Internal parasites	Ticks
Lice		

Spray cattle once a week during warm weather for flies and practice good sanitation. Lice can be controlled by spraying in late winter and early spring. Grubs may be controlled with an insecticide that can be applied as a dust, spray, pour-on or a systemic ingredient in the feed. Internal parasites can be controlled by a special liquid medication or by inclusion of these chemicals in mineral blocks. Dipping and spraying with an approved insecticide is the most effective method of controlling ticks. And remember, for ear ticks the chemical must be applied into the ear. Check with your veterinarian about having all these programs incorporated into your general preventative herd health program. And, do not ignore the importance of a rigid sanitation program.

Poisonous Plants

While we are discussing herd-health matters, we should make you aware that there are poisonous plants that may cause problems in your herd. Most poisonings are difficult to classify, because the plant may be poisonous only during certain seasons of the year or under unusual or special circumstances and the effects may be quite diverse. At one end of the spectrum the symptoms are barely discernible and may only be evidenced by unthriftiness, while at the other end, poisoning from some plants, can lead to death within an hour. Needless to say, cattle should not be permitted into suspect pastures. If there are poisonous weeds, eliminate them immediately. If that is impractical, only turn cattle out into pastures when the weed is relatively harmless. Pictorial weed-identification pamphlets may be obtained from your county agricultural agent. A conscientious weed-control program, both by mowing and the application of a herbicide, will control most of the plants poisonous to livestock.

There are many poisonous plants. Some of the most common are pictured below and on the following pages:

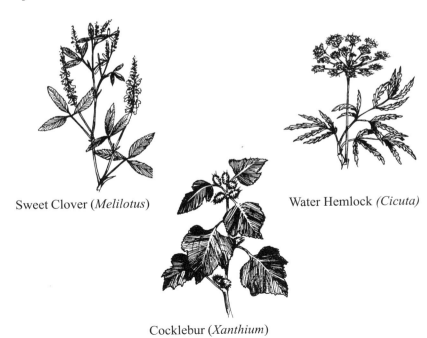

Sweet Clover (*Melilotus*)

Water Hemlock *(Cicuta)*

Cocklebur (*Xanthium*)

109

White Snake *(Eupatorium)*

Rape (*Brassica*)

Black Nightshade *(Solanum)*

Larkspur or Poisonweed *(Delphinium)*

Milkweed *(Asclepias)*

Goosefoot (*Halogeton*)

Locoweed (*Astragalus or Oxytropus*)

Oleander (*Nerium*)

Buttercup (*Ranunculus*)

Tarweed or Gumweed (*Grindelia*)

Corncockle (*Agrostemma*)

Lupine (*Lupinus*)

Indian Hemp (*Apocynum*)   Yew *(Taxus)*

Nutrition

Nutrition is another factor in the health of your herd. A good, balanced, full nutritional ration is essential for a healthy growing animal in a cow/calf operation. But, we also know that if you tend your pastures properly and have the grass in a nutritious, succulent form, and if hay, you have fertilized and harvested it on a timely basis, 85 percent of the job has been done. That is why the utilization of good pastures and other roughages is considered the very foundation for a successful beef-cattle operation. The other 15 percent would vary depending on innumerable factors but in one form or another would usually consist of concentrates or energy feeds, protein feeds and supplements, vitamins, mineral supplements and may even extend to growth stimulants and implants for feed efficiency.

If your operation is a large commercial one, you will undoubtedly have expert advice so handling this nutritional question will be technically basic to your operation. If you have a smaller cattle operation, go see your local feed dealer as he should be able to offer you advice and a premixed commercial feed to supplement your good pastures and hay.

A brief reminder: you will need a good cow/calf identification and record-keeping system. Each animal needs a permanent identification, either in the form of a tattoo or brand. From an operational point of view, a large eartag provides the best means to utilize meaningful data in the field or chute. For example, a color-coded system tied to a particular sire, plus the identification system, should give the year of birth and dam's number, thus becomes an easily readable age and parentage record. You may go one step further and include health records. We are also confident electronic tags will be commercially available and feasible supplying a full range of data that will be communicated directly between the ear tag and your computer or indirectly by the use of a modem. There are several identification systems in use, including the International Letter System which identifies the year of birth such as H for 1998. It's a good idea to check with your breed association for its requirements and preferences.

In keeping with the goals of the book, this chapter offers a creative way to explain, in a concise, crisp format, the annual operating program for a beef cattle herd. As you can imagine, or know by experience, we are talking about a tremendous amount of detailed information. Many excellent texts, some listed in the reference section, will explain in better detail than we can if you are so inclined to this recommended option. Do not forget your local veterinarian and your agricultural extension agent or beef cattle specialist—they can be an important source of information and guidance. Observe the operating practices of your respected breeders and the timing of each detail. Your fellow ranchers will be more than happy to share their experiences, and it's a great learning opportunity.

Annual Operating Program

We believe that an annual operating program for your beef herd involves the following sequences of activities and procedures. They are not ranch-specific. Your geographic area and your individual needs will influence the time, date and whether you use a particular procedure or system. Use this outline as a checklist. Because of the sequential presentation of the activities it will provide you a "feel" for the business. The sample starts at the beginning of the calendar year, but can be adjusted according to your operating schedule or geography.

A Sequential Annual Operating Program for Your Beef Herd

January

> Plan matings for the coming season
> Breed heifers for fall calving
> For fall calves, castrate males and dehorn as necessary
> Get bulls on proper ration for breeding
> Select and inventory spring sale cattle and get them on feed
> Order identification supplies such as ear tags
> Submit advertising copy for sale cattle

February

> Start breeding cows for late fall calves
> Review health papers of sale cattle for compliance
> Vaccinate fall calves for blackleg, malignant edema and any other disease your veterinarian deems necessary
> Begin fertilization of Coastal Bermuda grass (repeat after each hay cutting) and top-dress small grain/ryegrass pastures

March

> Breed for December/January calves
> Treat for grubs by either spray, pour-on or feed
> Introduce grain to fall calves
> Prepare for spring calving season
> Watch first-calf heifers for calving problems

April

> Separate cows and their fall bull calves from other cows
> Check with veterinarian regarding pre-weaning vaccinations

May

> Begin weaning fall calves
> Treat fall calves after weaning for parasites
> Separate all fall heifers from all bulls
> Begin spraying for flies

June

> Grade offspring—what stays, what goes, tag, tattoo or brand all remaining calves not done at birth

114

Annual blood test for brucellosis and tuberculosis—entire herd

Breed cows for spring calves

Vaccinate all heifers for Bang's (Brucellosis) disease

Vaccinate spring calves for blackleg, malignant edema and any other disease your veterinarian deems necessary

July

Initiate first steps to train bull calves for sale (broken to halter and to lead)

Remove bulls from cow herd

If necessary, buy hay

If registered, make out applications

August

Spray barns, pens, etc.

Select entries for feeder calf sales

Wean early spring calves from lean or run-down cows and treat for worms

Check with veterinarian regarding pre-weaning vaccinations

September

Before weaning, introduce calves to grain

Verify tattoo/tags of dam and offspring

Have bulls trimmed, priced and ready for sale

Examine your cows and their records for ease and percentage of calving

Test equipment for reliability and scales for accuracy

Seed small grains, ryegrass or legumes for winter/spring grazing

October

Wean spring calves from cows

Cull cows

Turn cattle in grain stubble fields if available

Weigh steers individually

Sell steers

Plan next year's advertising and promotional program

November

Spray for lice

Plan for winter conditions

Start feeding cows winter ration before breeding

Inventory for complete set of supplies, medicines, ID tags, and equipment, if necessary, order new supply

December

Arrange to have your veterinarian check for respiratory ailments

Spray for lice again

Take physical inventory of equipment, cattle, receipts, expenses, etc. and submit to CPA for tax purposes

Critique yearly program with family and all employees and reward accordingly

Prepare cash-flow budget for upcoming year, and revise overall business plan

Chapter 8

Marketing Beef Cattle

The marketing of your livestock is as important to your overall ranch program as the production segment. As we mentioned previously, our experience is that people knowledgeable in production tend to look at costs and efficiency while marketing types look to increase profits by marketing alone. In either case, they need the complement of the other, but in an integrated manner. You do not want to be in the awkward position of trying to sell whatever you produce rather than producing what the current market demands. A wise marketing approach begins in the breed/cattle selection stage, continues through the breeding, weaning and feeding/development stages of your production plan, and concludes with the sale of your cattle.

The nature of this discussion on marketing will focus on the general aspects that make for a successful and financially rewarding experience in the beef cattle business.

First, we assume you have a product that is currently accepted in the marketplace. This is easier said than done. Even with the best plans, market forces and idiosyncrasies change, such as cattle size or frame for example. Look back in the dedication and review the small frame of the Angus heifer presented to President Eisenhower—much too small for today's market. Subsequently, the market went through a period demanding larger and larger frames by selecting primarily for size or by introducing large continental breeds such as Simmental, Limousin, Chianina and others into the mix. Today, all we hear about is moderation in frame and the absence of ear or Brahman blood.

This brings up an interesting paradox. Modern cattle, supposedly structured by the current market and as proffered by the vocal cattle experts, should contain little, if any, Brahman influence. However, in one of the largest cattle shows and sales—the 1998 Houston Livestock Show—sale prices for purebred cattle reflected a different story. Brahman females averaged $10,500, while Simmental/Simbrah females averaged $2,488, Braunvieh females, $5,690 and Senepol females, $1,500. While these are average sale prices for purebred cattle, they do reflect the tendencies in the commercial market. Do they confirm the so-called informed or intelligent thinking? You be the judge.

This example underscores two principles we have stressed throughout the book: keep an open mind and rely on the facts.

Second, there are some important things a breeder can do to have a positive effect on the price you receive for your cattle. They include:

🐂 Raise good cattle—both in type and quality.

🐂 Select for uniformity in size, conformation, weight, age and color for each group of cattle. That is why the color black is so prevalent in beef cattle today. It is a dominant genetic attribution and it also plays off the positive black Angus reputation in the feeder and retail market.

🐂 If horned, remove horns completely at an early age by dehorning or by using a homozygously polled bull in your breeding program. Remember, both the color black and polledness are usually dominant traits.

✔ Have all cattle vaccinated for major diseases and treated for parasites. Showcase medical records to prospective buyers.

✔ Finish off your sale cattle a little. In the commercial market, heavier cattle usually bring more money. But, don't over-feed; it is a waste of time and money and you will probably be penalized in the marketplace for excess fat.

✔ Arrange, if practical, to sell your cattle during the most favorable time of the year. There are usually seasonal varia-tions in price. Keep this in mind when planning for the breeding season.

✔ Have your sale cattle fitted-out to a limited extent if they are registered, but whether or not they are registered, present them to good advantage. If you have culls, which every breeder should have, get rid of them before promoting your cattle. You will save money and your reputation by making a quick decision to sell them off the ranch. In addition, if you market your cattle from the ranch, have your pastures in top condition with good-looking and serviceable fences (Chapter Four—Eye Appeal). Remember, perception is subjective! Make the buyers' eyes work for you.

✔ Keep good production records to help you analyze your herd's breeding/market price relationship. The records can be used as a helpful tool in your marketing efforts.

If you adhere to the preceding suggestions, you should have a product that is in demand in the market. The next consideration in your marketing plan, which we believe to be as important as the above is promotion. Actually, promotion, promotion and promo-tion! This is why some beef cattle receive more than a price deter-mined solely by weight and market price per pound. Sales and sale price are a function of product-value and promotion. Each side of the equation needs quality for overall success in the mar-ketplace. This is why the Leachman family's 1998 Red Angus regis-tered bull sale in Montana had an average sale price of $12,570, and an overall gross of $4,800,000 for all cattle—a bellwether dol-lar scenario in any livestock comparison. The Leachmans have ex-cellent beef cattle, and religiously practice the above list of sugges-tions. But we believe that the significantly higher values they ob-tain in the marketplace can be attributed to the overwhelming repu-tation of Leachman cattle fortified by their unique and successful brand of promotion. They did it years ago at Ankony with Angus cattle and after selling the herd repeated the adventure with Red Angus. Now they are having an influence on other breeds and prominent breeders by bringing their intellect and marketing prowess to other beef cattle programs. The Leachman case history is an outstanding example of the process of evaluating the market, developing the product and then promoting it to its highest level.

While we acknowledge the preceding example is partly a highly specialized purebred operation, the principle definitely applies to the commercial cow/calf producer as well. The reason is that ranchers who have developed a reputation for good, healthy, uniform cattle of the right type, almost always receive a premium in the marketplace. The reputation of the ranch for its cattle, in the minds of cattle buyers and packers is influenced to a large extent by consistency in product and serious promotion. As described previously under the Angus section, the success of the Certified Angus Beef Program is a commercial example of such a product:promotion interrelationship. Promotion, we believe, should be the cornerstone of your ranching and beef-cattle program. We suggest you examine and analyze the promotional programs of the top beef-cattle breeders, and possibly adapt some of their tools to develop a program for your ranch. Attend some of the major livestock shows to see how the breeders present their cattle, and examine the literature. All the major breeds will be represented by their respective breeders association, and members will be pleased to answer your questions and share their literature and trade journals. If needed and feasible, enlist the aid of an experienced beef-cattle marketing/advertising specialist. Or investigate forming a joint venture with a well-known and compatible producer, who can help you in marketing and promoting your cattle. Most of the prominent breeders have such joint-venture programs involving cattle, not real estate. Be sure they have an excellent reputation for honesty, integrity, loyalty and outstanding cattle. A joint venture may be a good way for a neophyte to enter the business. In fact, that's what we did when we first entered the industry.

The following definitions are useful for the new weekend cowboy entering the commercial market:

- *Type* is a dominant and subjective characteristic of the individual animal. It changes with market preferences and is an important consideration in your breeding program. In general, type refers to the ideal standard of form and structure, such as great width and depth of body, that contributes to an animal's value for a specific purpose. Today, type reflects whether a steer, or heifer is small, compact or growthy with good bone and substance. While these and other type characters can be measured or quantified, people generally have a subjective vision of the ideal type for their specific purpose.

- *Market class* is a grouping determined: (1) by age and are classified such as cattle, calves, yearlings, two-year-olds; (2) by the use to which the livestock will be put, such as slaughter, feeder, or stocker; and (3) by sex—steers, heifers, cows, or bulls.

- *Market grades* are more familiar to the layperson because they reflect quality designations of the carcass and shoppers see the top grades in specific cuts of meat. Grades are primarily determined by market preferences and valuation. However, in practical terms, they indirectly judge variations in the taste of beef by gauging the degree of marbling or intramuscular fat and its maturity. But remember, market preferences do change. Health-conscious consumers desire for leaner beef during the last decade has prompted many producers to change their breeding programs by introducing continental breed genetics into their herd or by using EPDs for low-marbling types. In 1998, we read that the pendulum has started to swing back. Major fast-food restaurants have started to retreat from the lean beef and low-fat fare. While fast-food restaurants represent a specialty or niche market, the return to fattier foods does seem to reflect consumer demands and preferences. A confirmation of this market change is being verified by the major cereal and food producers; low- or reduced-fat products are not selling as well as they have in the past and consequently are taking up less shelf space. Perhaps the trend means a more dichotomous market for beef. In any event, keep abreast of consumer preferences in a changing world and design your product for current and future market requirements. The selection for proper genetics and management inputs will go a long way in satisfying these ever changing market demands. In concluding this paragraph on market grades, it may be of interest to know that the descending order of quality are prime, choice, select, standard, utility, cutter and canner.

⌇ *Yield grades* also exist. They are determined by the yield or percentage of lean meat obtained from a carcass. This system is becoming prevalent and probably more so in the future, as packers and good producers find this a more effective way to determine the true economic value of cattle. Yield grades are determined by differences in the percentage of lean meat obtained from a carcass. They are represented in descending order of desirability, from one to five.

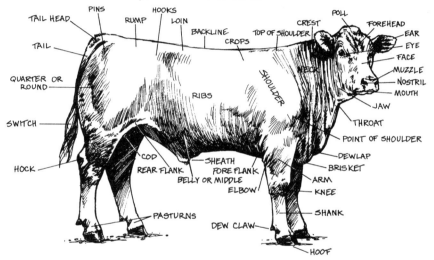

In our discussion, we believe your goal should be to produce an animal whose carcass will grade out in the top two classifications in both quality and yield. This is important because high grades will contribute to higher selling prices and is an indication of better palatability of the meat. Remember, it costs essentially the same to feed and maintain a low-grade animal as it does a higher-grade one. By producing better beef, you not only have the direct effect of a better rate of return on your feed ration, but you will also contribute significantly to the reputation of your ranch.

Finally, we believe it may be helpful to mention the marketing channels or methods usually used to market beef cattle. They can be classified several ways, but for simplicity, we categorize the methods as follows:

- *Private Treaty:* In our opinion private treaty is one of the most financially and emotionally rewarding ways to market your cattle. It involves the buyer coming to the producer's ranch, inspecting the cattle and together agreeing on a negotiated price. In so doing, you have more control over the many factors that indirectly influence buyer perceptions—and ultimately the price and the time frame in which you sell your product. The suggestions we made previously, have good cattle, segregate into eye appealing lots, have ranch looking successful and prosperous, all contribute to your reputation. And reputation is extremely important in private treaty sales. Buyers are usually attracted to your ranch because of your reputation with other cattlemen, your breed association, advertisements in trade journals, seeing your cattle in performance test demonstrations, or simply observing your cattle in your lush, eye-appealing pastures. Finally, insure that all health records are available, and if applicable, breeding and production records. While you may also use other methods of marketing, the private treaty method, conducted on your ranch, enables you a tremendous show window for your herd—an overall good way to promote and market your cattle.

- *Auction Market*—At this type of market, your cattle are sold to the highest bidder based on either price per head or price per hundredweight. Auctions may take the form of a consignment, production, herd reduction or herd dispersal sale. The consignment sale is generally sponsored by the local, state or national breed or cattle associations. Besides using the auction market as a means for immediate income, auctions provide a platform to showcase your cattle before the public and hence help establish your reputation.

- *Video Market*—The video method enables you, for a modest video fee, to expose your sale cattle to a wide spectrum of potential buyers. Currently, this method is not truly applicable to the purebred or registered cattle business, because the system has not developed the data format and three dimensional profile needed to purchase breeding cattle. But this technique probably only needs more development and sophistication in its form and substance.

- *Internet*—We currently do not know an active Internet market for beef cattle. However, we do think this technique, using other electronic devices, such as easy-to-use digital cameras and low-cost scanners, provides a new paradigm to market cattle. Marketing cattle on the Internet appears to be ideally suited to the geographic diverse and expansive nature of buyers and sellers of beef cattle. In addition, the cost efficiencies in marketing cattle through this technology should be welcomed by all segments of the industry. It is estimated by the commerce department that in several years, electronic commerce on the Internet should approach $300 billion. We expect the marketing of live beef cattle to be an important part of this new method of buying and selling.

Part Three:

An Exotic Diversion

Chapter 9

Pecans

General Considerations

After all the chores are done, and the cattle are peacefully grazing on lush green pastures, you will need an intellectual or tranquil diversion from the everyday regime. Your ranching and leisure activities may even be fodder for conversation at cocktail and dinner parties back in the big city. Different activities will extend your own life by making it more interesting and enjoyable, and who knows, maybe you will even make a buck. For *Country Properties*, we selected pecans for our extracurricular activity, although grapes and wine-making may be equally enjoyable.

We were first introduced to pecan culture when Helen, a sister of our good friend, Dr. Ghent Graves, Jr, married Deane Stahmann, Jr. and left Houston, Texas for Las Cruces, New Mexico. Deane's father had developed a 4,000-acre pecan grove in 1932—a brash move at the time. In so doing, he developed a new type of pecan culture in the desert valleys of the Southwest. This new culture, which we call, western irrigated culture, utilizes irrigation in the low-humidity desert valleys, and higher-density plantings, supplemented with renewal pruning. An interesting outgrowth of this western migration of pecan culture has been the development of new varieties that could not be previously grown in the eastern areas because of the higher humidity and their susceptibility to scab and other foliar diseases. By chance, genetic intervention, or luck, these new varieties also mature sooner, are smaller in size, and can be pruned. They are a "fit," with the higher-density plantings common within this new culture.

Some years later our interest in pecans was rekindled when our company, Weatherford International, now listed on the New York Stock Exchange, acquired another company. Its inventory included a 15,000-acre irrigated ranch in West Texas. At the time, that ranch was leased for agricultural purposes and returned enough to pay for the property taxes and insurance. The board decided to explore and examine the various ways to maximize the cash flow from this almost hidden asset. The location prevented it from being a hot real estate prospect, but it did have copious amounts of good soil and water. We remembered the Stahmann Farm to the west, and followed the advice we have already shared. We contacted Bluefford Hancock, the horticulture extension specialist at Texas A & M. This was the first time we had met him, but he made a favorable impression. His enthusiasm, knowledge and help proffered were contagious. But, the most long-lasting impression Bluefford left with us was the introduction to Professor Fred Brison. Professor Brison was professor of horticulture at Texas A & M University and had written, *Pecan Culture,* the only text on the subject. He was justly acclaimed, recognized and honored for all his contributions in the pecan industry. However, we best remember him for his ability to put his ideas and opinions in succinct, yet unforgiving form. We learned some basic principles from him, such as the importance of soil for most agricultural endeavors, in a way that we had not comprehended from taking more than twenty hours of soil courses in our bachelor and Ph.D. programs. Professor Brison had a unique way of explaining concepts, whether in a lecture hall or on the bank of a stream as we were looking at a soil profile. And he taught anyone who was willing to listen.

We have elaborated because the pecan industry, like the ranching and cattle industry, developed due to market demand. These developments were greatly influenced and directed by some great individual advocates of the pecan like Professors Brison, Hancock, Benton Storey and lately George McEachern, a former graduate student of Professor Hancock. They loved what they were doing, and the industry today reflects their contributions and love for it.

Types

There are two types of pecans— the so-called native pecans, here on earth solely because of the Lord, and the improved varieties where man had his hand in the formula.

Native: Native trees grow in Texas, Georgia, Oklahoma, Louisiana, Arkansas, Mississippi, Kansas, Missouri, Kentucky, Tennessee, Illinois, Indiana, Iowa, Nebraska, South and North Carolina and Florida. While there are improved varieties growing in all the preceding states, the recent impetus has been in pushing the cultural range further west into West Texas, western Oklahoma, New Mexico, Arizona, and to a limited extent, into California and Mexico.

If your new ranch happens to have some large, healthy native trees, you are indeed fortunate. Sooner or later you will want to bring them into top form and production and for this we refer you to Professor Brison's excellent text, *Pecan Culture* or the *Texas Pecan Handbook*. In addition, there are many extension service and USDA pamphlets on technicalities such as grafting or topworking. The free booklets are available, at your local county agricultural agent's office, normally located in the county seat. Or you may obtain information and advice from the state horticultural extension agent located at your state agricultural college and experiment station. In case you get bitten by this contagious bug, the pecan, and want to develop a pecan grove, read on.

Improved Varieties: Good varieties are a necessary adjunct to good soil and climate for the successful production of pecans. The varieties must be adapted and proven in the geographical area where they are grown. It is largely on the basis of their adaptation to climate and susceptibility to scab disease that they are classified as Western, Eastern or Northern varieties. Significant advancements in varietal improvement have been made during the last forty years. The tree and nut characteristics of the new improved varieties which are considered desirable are described as follows.

Tree Characteristics

Precociousness: The tree should commence bearing good annual crops of quality nuts at an early age.

Prolific Growth: Vigor in growth is usually associated with high yields; consequently, large dense foliage is important for consistent production of good quality nuts.

Short Growth Cycle: Late spring growth with early maturity of nuts minimizes frost damage and provides for early marketability of the crop. In addition, early nut maturity enables the leaves to have more time to rebuild food reserves of the tree so that it may bloom and set a crop of nuts the following year.

Disease Resistance: Resistance to diseases of the pecan such as scab.

Capability of Being Pruned without Loss of Bearing: This is a necessity for intensified, high-density type culture due to the need to control size. Emotionally, this is difficult to do, but it is essential to the grove's future.

Favorable Branching Habit: Trees should have wide-angle crotches because they are stronger and carry crops better.

Nut Characteristics

Size: Large with a range of forty-five to sixty pecans per pound.

Desirable Kernel: The kernels should be plump and have good flavor, little fiber or "fuzz," a light or bright color, a smooth surface and good keeping qualities.

Desirable Shell: Internally, there should be no central partition septum. Shells should be attractive in appearance and crack easily.

Varieties by Geographic Area:

The varieties listed below constitute the reservoir of well-tested and adapted varieties that are available for use in the three geographic areas where pecans are grown. However, check with your agricultural extension agent for the latest recommendations. Note, there is some overlapping of areas and varieties.

Western Irrigated Area:

Apache is a cultivar that has good tree vigor and production. The nut is medium-size, of good quality, and contains 58 percent to 60 percent kernel. This variety will shell satisfactorily and the keeping quality of the kernel is good—not in popular demand.

Burkett is included here because of historical significance. A chance seedling but used in many breeding or crossing programs. It is highly susceptible to scab and not recommended for new plantings.

Cheyenne is a variety that appears to be outstanding for the Western area and it is a perfect pollinator for the Wichita variety. The tree is precocious, prolific, relatively resistant to scab and responds well to pruning. The nut has outstanding shelling characteristics, is of medium-size and contains approximately 58 percent kernel. However, it is highly susceptible to aphid infestations but its outstanding kernel characteristics outweigh this deficiency.

Comanche is a pecan out of favor today. The tree is vigorous, has good foliage but is susceptible to scab and downy spot. The nut is very large, of good quality and usually contains 52 percent to 60 percent kernel. Tendency for forked branching is a disadvantage of the variety.

Kiowa is a variety that had great expectations as the nut is of high quality and usually contains 58 percent kernel. However, recent experience has shown that older trees have not performed up to snuff and consequently is not recommended for new plantings.

Osage is a relative newcomer to the ranks. The nut is small, round and smooth but of high quality and it ripens extremely early in the season. The foliage is considered attractive and the variety is recommended for the northern reaches of the Western region.

Pawnee is best known for its nut, which is early maturing, high quality, medium size and approximately 58 percent kernel. The tree is not precocious, but does have attractive dark green foliage and exhibits some resistance to aphid infestations. It is recommended for all portions of the Western region and is also considered an excellent yard tree.

San Saba Improved is an older variety that has a sentimental niche to Texas pecan growers. It is not precocious but trees produce well and consistently when older. The nut is medium-size, of good quality and contains 55 percent to 60 percent kernel. Its shelling properties are good. However, it is not recommended at this time for new plantings.

Shawnee appears to be out of favor with growers today. While not precocious, it is scab-tolerant in the Western area and well-suited for higher density plantings. It appears to be a good commercial shelling type and is acceptable for the in-shell trade.

Shoshoni is a high-producing pecan, but its biggest appeal is the early maturity of the nut. The nut is medium to large size and contains about 58 percent kernel. It is precocious and needs some time for the tree to mature properly. It is recommended for the northern reaches of the Western region.

Sioux is best known for its attractive kernels. They are perceived in the marketplace to be more attractive than any other pecan variety. While the pecan nut is small, the tree exhibits good vigor with heavy and consistent yields. In low-humidity areas it is an excellent yard tree.

Western is the variety that made the West, at least in pecan parlance. It is precocious, prolific, vigorous with extremely heavy and consistent production. In addition, it is suitable for close spacing and pruning while still remaining a very attractive tree. This variety will shell well, and the keeping quality of the kernel is good. This variety is puzzling because it tends to do better than other varieties with a lower level of management.

Wichita is the darling of horticulturists. It is like a fine-tuned Indy 500 car—fast, capable of making a lot of money, and looks beautiful. But, like the race car, it requires precise management and execution. This is the best Western-type variety available for intensified culture; and will cross-pollinate well with Western, San Saba Improved and Cheyenne. However, it is highly susceptible to scab and requires an intensive irrigation schedule plus increased nitrogen and zinc fertilizations. The nut is medium-sized, of good color, and has a high percentage of kernel.

Major Eastern Cultivars:

Caddo is an excellent quality, shelling pecan with sixty to seventy-five nuts per pound, and a 52–58 kernel percentage. It is precocious, has excellent foliage, good scab resistance and the nut ripens early. The tree is good for early-flowering cultivars.

Choctaw was once a highly recommended variety, but has fallen on hard times as nuts from older trees appear to be of lessor quality. The tree is vigorous and in most cases resistant to scab. It needs intensive management, and because it is a large tree, needs space. It is not recommended for new plantings.

Desirable is the counterpart in the southeastern states to the Western variety in the western growing area. It has a long history of producing heavy yields of well-filled nuts. The tree is not precocious, is susceptible to scab, but has been a winner in the Gulf Coast with the application of foliar fungicides.

Houma is a relatively new pecan variety that has excellent disease resistance and a high-quality, medium-sized nut. Suggested for use in the high-humidity areas.

Mahan is a somewhat controversial variety and is not recommended for new plantings. However, it has some grass-roots affection among pecan growers probably because of its extremely large-size nut. The variety tends to overbear, is precocious, prolific with excellent tree vigor and foliage, but it is susceptible to scab. It is used almost exclusively for the in-shell market.

Mohawk is a Mahan relative with a large nut. It is precocious and exhibits prolific growth, but is susceptible to scab disease. It is considered more of a shade tree variety today. It is not currently recommended for new plantings.

Oconee is a new variety developed in Georgia for the humid areas as it is resistant to scab. The tree appears to be productive and the kernel is of high quality.

Shawnee is considered a good shelling pecan because it has no fuzz on the kernels. The tree is precocious, a prolific grower and depending on the area somewhat tolerant to scab. Today, it is mostly a yard tree.

Stuart is an old and popular pecan variety in the Southeast in spite of the many negative characteristics it carries, such as susceptibility to disease and its tendency to be slow to come into bearing. It is also a moderate producer of average or below-average nuts. This variety is not now recommended for new plantings.

Northern Area:

The northern range of the pecan industry is able to utilize fewer varieties. Here, resistance to frost and cold plays an important role.

Colby is a vigorous pecan, a heavy pollen producer and considered an early nut producer. It is an Illinois seedling and thus does well in that environment.

Giles is a Kansas seedling variety. It is precocious, prolific and produces fairly large high-quality pecans.

Major, a Kentucky seedling, is probably the most popular northern variety. It bears well, has good foliage and produces an average-sized nut.

Maramec is a newer variety trying to find its place in the northern area of Texas and Oklahoma. The tree is attractive but the quality of the kernel is only average.

Peruque, a Missouri seedling, has good vigor and foliage, bears early and well and the nut has a very thin shell.

Posey is an Indiana seedling, with excellent nut characteristics and kernel quality. It needs high fertility to bear well but is a good pollen producer.

Site Selection

The site you select for your grove is the most important consideration you will make, since the growth and fruiting of pecan trees depend upon it. Various factors that influence or are a function of the site may be classified as follows:

Soil Factors: Good soil is essential for successful pecan production. It should be deep, loose, moisture-retentive, but well drained, with no impervious clay layers.

Soil fertility is not as important as the physical characteristics of a pecan grove. Most soils in the United States, except the very sandy ones, are supplied with the necessary elements for tree growth, except for nitrogen. This can be added in the form of nitrogen fertilizer. Other elements, which are occasionally lacking in soil, such as potassium and zinc, also can be applied.

Pecan trees are somewhat indifferent to alkalinity and acidity of soils. They grow satisfactorily where pH values range from 5 to 8.5. However, adverse effects of zinc deficiency, which result in pecan rosette, are more severe with alkaline soils.

In the irrigated areas, pay attention to the sodium content of the soil and water. Sodium creates problems with the soil's structure, and ultimately, its drainage. In addition, salinity, reduces tree growth and nut production. Often the effects are seen within a year or two after transplanting. In evaluating and selecting your site for pecan production, be sure to have your soil, and irrigation water analyzed for sodium content. The results will be expressed as SAR, the sodium absorption ratio. If the values are above 3.0, find another location or seek professional guidance.

Climatic Factors: There are four components of the climate that are important for proper growing conditions: 1) length of growing season, 2) temperature, 3) amount of moisture, and 4) humidity.

Length of the Growing Season: The pecan requires a long frost-free period from spring until fall for the normal maturity of the nut. The actual number of days required varies amongst varieties from 150 to 240 days.

Temperature: This is the most important climatic factor affecting pecan culture. It not only determines the length of the growing season, but also influences the type of vegetative growth. Pecans grow best where the average summer temperatures are within 75 to 85 degrees Fahrenheit, without extreme variations between day and night. Temperatures within this range are favorable for continuous growth and logically are called "continual growing temperatures." Temperatures that fall outside this range, or that have a wide variation between the daily maximum and minimum, favor sporadic growth—a limiting factor in pecan culture. In addition, the pecan tree has a chilling requirement which is essential if the tree is to flower and leaf out properly in the spring. The actual requirement is unknown, however, 400 to 750 hours of temperatures at or below 45 degrees F are thought to be essential. In Texas, the lower latitudinal limits appear to be located around Eagle Pass, Texas.

Moisture: Adequate soil moisture is necessary for growth and maturity of the nut. Moisture deficiency may cause the outer extremities of branches to die back, retard tree growth or even cause the death of the tree. Dryness can reduce nut size if rainfall is deficient in July and August when nuts are completing their growth, and can reduce nut fillings if deficient in late summer or early fall. The precise moisture requirement varies with sites and year, but it is generally believed that pecans require at least seven acre inches of moisture per month during the growing season or fifty inches of moisture per year. However, excessive water can also be detrimental, particularly standing water and elevated water tables.

Humidity: High relative-humidity negatively affects the pecan in the following ways by: 1) hindering effective pollination, 2) increasing the severity of most diseases, and 3) causing the premature sprouting of nuts in the husks. However, data shows a tremendous amount of nut production throughout the South, an area with high humidity.

Grove Design and Tree Spacing

Spatial: There are many possible designs for establishing pecan groves. The most popular and practical are the square, rectangular, and the square and rectangular with a temporary tree on the diagonal. During the last two to three decades, there has been a radical change in the number of pecan trees planted per acre. Formerly, almost all pecans were planted at distances between trees which were thought to be sufficient to give adequate spacing for sunlight and moisture absorption throughout the commercial life of the grove. Currently, initial tree plantings in the non-irrigated areas are usually made at spacings of 50' x 50', 60' x 60', 70' x 70', or 100' x 100'. Plantings in the western irrigated area are commonly planted 35' x 35'. Some plantings using precocious and prolific varieties have been established at spacings of 15' x 30', 25' x 25', 30' x 30', and 17.5' x 35'. These high-density plantings must be thinned at a later date when crowding becomes a problem. A system of training and pruning to control tree size is absolutely necessary.

The principal reason for planting more trees per acre is to get the grove into heavy production and on a paying basis more quickly. In financial terms, this is to increase the rate of return. It has been demonstrated in the western irrigated area that yields of young pecan trees are practically the same per tree for the first ten years with as high a density as seventy-one trees per acre (17.5' x 35').

With the precocious and prolific new varieties, such as Wichita, now available, groves on good soils with good water and management often will pay all expenses of the operation as quickly as the fourth or fifth year after planting. By a progressive system of gradual removal of excess trees, or pruning to control tree size, the yields per acre can gradually be increased until the grove reaches relative maturity.

However, today this philosophy is being reexamined. This is a classic example of the intellectual battle between pure horticulturists and economists. Both make good points, but you must be reconciled to the fact that this type of system will not produce long-lived productive trees.

This is analogous to a father explaining the fun and consequences of playing football. In the beginning, football is enjoyable, brings recognition and maybe even large sums of money. Later in life, however, you probably can't walk without pain. Your bad neck generates soreness and restriction of movement in your arms and shoulders, and there are miscellaneous other problems that limit or play havoc with your lifestyle. Depending on your philosophy you make an almost irreconcilable decision with long-term and serious implications.

Pollination: One other consideration must be given to grove design and this involves the subject of pollination. The pecan produces imperfect flowers with the staminate or pollen-bearing flower produced on the last season's growth and the pistillate or female flowers borne at the terminals of new, current season growth. Some varieties develop the staminate flowers (catkins) early, and the pollen can be shed before the pistillate flowers become receptive (protandrous). Other varieties develop the pistillate flowers early and they become receptive before the pollen is shed (protogynous). In most varieties the periods of pollen shedding and pistil receptivity extend for several days and may, under normal conditions, overlap sufficiently to insure pollination. More commonly the two periods are partially or completely distinct. To plan for proper pollination in a grove, care should be taken to ensure that both protandrous and protogynous types are planted. The most popular named varieties are classified as follows:

Protandrous	Protogynous
Caddo	Apache
Cheyenne	Burkett
Desirable	Choctaw
Giles	Colby
Houma	Comanche
Major	Kiowa
Pawnee	Mahan
Peruque	Maramec
Oconee	Mohawk
Osage	Posey
San Saba Improved	Shawnee
Western	Shoshoni
	Sioux
	Stuart
	Wichita

Grove Establishment

Methods: There are three methods for establishing a planted pecan grove.

1) Plant budded or grafted nursery trees. The planting of good sound nursery stock of adapted pecan varieties is the preferred way to establish the grove. Such trees under good management develop an intensive root system and will give a uniform planting. The optimum size for pecan nursery stock is from five to eight feet high. This will usually represent a three- to four-year old rootstock and a one- or two-year scion variety, or top. The use of larger nursery stock offers no increased benefit and is more expensive.

2) Plant seedling trees. An economical practice in establishing a pecan grove is to use seedling trees. The trees are grown from seed in a nursery and are transplanted in exactly the same manner as budded nursery stock. After they are well established, they can be budded or grafted to the desired variety. This procedure offers several advantages: the initial cost of the trees is less; you have approximately three years to determine what varieties you want in the planting and the trunk has a tendency to develop better.

Suffice to say, that in the propagation of improved varieties, various types of patch-budding, are suggested for small pecan seedlings running up to approximately 1.5 inches in diameter. Seedlings, 1.5 inches and larger, may be propagated by using the inlay-graft technique. Inasmuch as the actual propagation of nursery stock is outside the realm of this discussion, please refer to any standard text on plant propagation or the *Texas Pecan Handbook* for the details involved in these techniques.

3) Plant nuts in place. Usually three to five nuts are placed where a tree is desired. The objective is to get one seedling tree to each location, then it is budded or grafted to an improved variety. It usually takes about three to four years to get a tree at all locations and this results in a very nonuniform planting. This is an inexpensive method, but it requires at least three or four additional years to get a grove into production. Additionally, there appears to be no basis for the theory that seedlings developed from nuts planted in place have superior root systems.

Clonal Propagation: A recent development in the field of pecan propagation warrants mention. This development entails new methods, which permit the clonal propagation of pecan rootstocks. Normally a pecan tree is propagated by budding or grafting the chosen scion variety onto a seedling rootstock. Seedlings are a sexual product and are therefore inherently variable, especially in a very heterozygous tree such as the pecan. Small but significant differences in such factors as the vigor, yield, and uniformity of the scion variety can be expected when seedling rootstocks are used. These and other inherent disadvantages of seedling stocks have been recognized for many years.

A clonal rootstock, on the other hand, is vegetatively propagated using a vegetative portion of the parent tree (similar to the new clonal reproduction of sheep and cattle mentioned earlier). Thus, the progeny from any one tree or selection will maintain the character of that selection and be true-to-type.

Three potential advantages are envisioned if a commercial clonal method is developed to propagate pecan rootstock:

1) Adaptation of pecan trees to certain soil limitations. In the semiarid and arid Southwest, chloride toxicity and zinc fixation in the irrigated soils are usually a problem. Researchers at Texas A & M have selected seedlings that largely exclude chloride ions and

also have demonstrated that pecan seedlings vary greatly in their efficiency at extracting zinc from the soil solution. If these seedling selections could be clonally propagated, and kept true-to-type, standard varieties budded onto them should perform better on saline and alkaline soils, lowering production costs and increasing yields.

2) The possibility exists that dwarfing rootstocks along the lines of the Malling and Malling-Merton clonal apple stocks could be selected for the pecan. Such stocks, if commercially feasible, would allow high-density plantings with less need for pruning. Yields per acre should be substantially increased and greater precocity might result. Here again, selected dwarfing stocks must be maintained true-to-type by clonal or vegetative propagation.

3) Clonal rootstocks would greatly reduce the tree-to-tree variability which exists in pecan groves. This would be particularly valuable in grove evaluation because of the knowledge that all trees would be genetically identical.

As exciting and beneficial as this sounds we do not see much research work being performed on this subject—maybe money or politics have something to do with it.

Transplanting and Training: Proper transplanting and training of the pecan tree is one of the most important practices in grove management. The basic steps were given to us by B.G. Hancock of Texas A & M University.

1) Obtain good trees—it sounds simple and logical but you can seldom make a silk purse out of a sow's ear, nor can you produce a good productive pecan tree from inferior stock. Sturdy, vigorous trees from a reliable nursery source must be used. The root system should be free of crown gall and nematode damage and the top should be well grown and be identified correctly as to the variety.

Three- to- four-year-old trees, with one- to- two-year-old tops, may be from four to eight feet high. Moderate-sized nursery trees will suffer less "transplant shock" and usually will become established and grow faster than large trees.

2) Keep the root system slightly moist at all times prior to planting. Dampen packing media when trees arrive and plant immediately or place in cold storage. If trees must be held for a long period, heel them in with moist soil.

3) Trim the root system. Cut off all broken and bruised roots with sharp shears or a knife. Most new roots develop on side roots and not more than ten inches from the top.

4) Prune the top portion of the tree, one-third to one-half, to compensate for the loss of a major part of the functioning root system when the tree was dug.

5) Dig hole—it should be just wide and deep enough to accommodate the root system of the tree without bending any of the roots. A power-driven auger, twelve to eighteen inches in diameter, is an excellent implement for digging the holes.

6) Plant the tree at the same depth as it stood in the nursery row. Arrange roots in their natural position. Fill the hole about three-fourths full of friable top soil and work the soil around the roots. Pour approximately five gallons of water into the hole to settle the soil, eliminate the air pockets and keep the roots moist.

7) Finish filling the hole with loose topsoil. Leave soil unpacked on surface to allow easy penetration of water.

8) Water the young tree. Keeping optimum soil moisture levels in the root zone is highly essential during the first season. The soil around the tree should be kept free of weeds and grass and the surface should be kept friable.

9) Training the young tree during the first and second growing seasons is vitally important to its future growth patterns and development. You should permit all shoots above the union to grow after the severe pruning at transplanting, but select and encourage one shoot to be the central leader. This "trashy trunk" method of training will protect the trunk from sunscald and wind damage. It will make the trunk increase in diameter and strengthen it at a much faster rate. If the shoots on the lower portion of the trunk are excessively vigorous, pinch-prune the terminal growing point. Be sure to cut off all water sprouts or suckers that develop below the bud union.

Eliminate "Y" crotches by cutting one of the forks back or completely off. This is particularly important for the Wichita variety. Correct "crow's feet" crotches, where three or more limbs arise near the same point, by leaving one growing intact and then cut the others back or off.

10) Prune the pecan tree by continuing to eliminate "Y" crotches and "crow's feet" as the tree grows. This will help build strong wide angle crotches. The top, at the end of the second or third growing season after transplanting, can shade the trunk and will be strong enough to withstand wind so that the branches on the lower part of the trunk may be removed. The desired height of the permanent lower limbs on a pecan tree will be determined by the climate, spacing and cultural procedures. It usually is not advisable to have permanent scaffold limbs lower than four to six feet.

A pecan tree that is trained correctly in the early growing seasons should develop a good system of scaffolded limbs. This strong framework of branches can withstand the elements of weather and the weight of heavy crop loads.

Production Practices

After you have established your grove and trained your trees, you have to initiate and maintain good cultural practices for high-quality production. Fertilization, insect, disease and weed control, coupled with selected pruning, are all vitally important to the success of the venture.

Fertilization: The following are general comments on fertilization for young and bearing trees. You should check with your county agricultural agent for specific recommendations.

Young Trees. Beginning with the second season, apply a nitrogenous fertilizer in a split schedule; the first in late winter, the second in late May or early June. The soil's texture, structure and fertility level will determine the amount of nitrogen. Because of the limited root system and top growth of the young tree, it is not advisable to exceed one-half pound of actual nitrogen per tree at each application. The fertilizer should be applied in a six- to ten-inch wide band. The inside of this band should start just inside the outer perimeter of the planting hole. In no case should nitrogenous fertilizer be applied closer than twelve inches to the tree trunk.

The application of foliar sprays containing zinc should be made to the young trees when the leaves are about one-third grown. Use zinc nitrate liquid (17% Zn) at the rate of one quart per 100 gallons of water. These applications are usually made every two weeks during the growing season, but be sure to commence early—about one week after bud break.

Bearing Trees. Research and extensive experience have shown that in most instances the only two nutrient elements that can be supplemented to increase pecan production are nitrogen and zinc. How much to apply is determined by soil and leaf analysis, but it must be correlated to tree growth and productivity.

There is a direct relationship between tree growth and pecan production. Tree growth can be measured in a number of ways but historically, it has usually been done by counting the number of leaves produced or by measuring the increase in trunk diameter or circumference.

One of the easiest methods to determine the growth of pecan trees, is to observe the length of the terminal growth of limbs. This measurement can be used in conjunction with a soil test to arrive at a satisfactory rate of fertilizer to be applied. The optimum rate of terminal growth on a bearing pecan tree is seven to fifteen inches per year. A tree showing this amount of growth should receive an application of only enough nitrogen to maintain this rate. A pecan tree that makes six inches or less of terminal growth per year will not produce regular crops of well-filled nuts. A tree in this deficient category should receive up to four one-pound applications of ammonium sulfate (21% N) per diameter inch of tree trunk to stimulate a more vigorous rate of growth. Ammonium nitrate (33.5% N) or urea (42% N) may also be used, but make sure you recalculate your application rate with the increased percent of actual nitrogen. For healthy trees, we recommend 60 to 200 pounds of nitrogen per acre per season, applied in three- to four- periodic applications of one-sixth pound of actual nitrogen per inch of the tree's diameter, beginning at bud break and continuing at monthly intervals.

Some years back we visited a cutting-edge type grove in Sahuarita, Arizona with Professors Bluefford Hancock and Benton Storey. It was a very large grove planted essentially with all the Wichita variety and irrigated with local water from wells. The yearly growth was phenomenal! Our recollection is that the terminal growth was up to four feet per year, but the trees were weak with poor structure. The air in the grove was highly humid, even in such a desert environment. The culprit was a previously unknown high level of nitrogen in the irrigation water. In addition, the growers had heavily fertilized the grove. This was a good example of too much nitrogen and too much growth.

Most all bearing pecan trees can benefit and should receive a scheduled foliar application of zinc as outlined in the paragraph about young trees. A tank mixture containing two pounds of liquid zinc nitrate (17% Zn) plus three pints of liquid nitrogen (32% N) is equally or more effective. Regardless of formulation or mix, applications should be made five times, at two-week intervals, beginning at green tip.

Irrigation and Drainage: We have mentioned that pecans need about fifty to fifty-five inches of moisture per year. And we've noted that a well-managed irrigation program, which minimizes moisture stress, also benefits most pecan programs. In the semiarid and desert areas, adequate irrigation is essential for successful pecan production. In most other areas, supplemental irrigation encourages high-quality nut production and reduces the severity of alternate bearing.

Apply water to the grove by one, or a combination, of the following methods: surface, drip, or sprinkler. Regardless of the method, the water system must be well planned, designed and constructed. There are many good publications and professional engineers to help you in this endeavor, so we will not belabor the subject here. We will, however, discuss a much-neglected topic and one as equally important as irrigation—namely, drainage and salinity management.

Drainage in agricultural lands is somewhat analogous to coronary artery disease in humans—a silent killer! It is amazing to see how little attention is paid to poor drainage and high water tables by people who should know better. Professors, agricultural producers, and even the international lending and technical assistance institutions, such as the World Bank, and FAO tend to make drainage low priority. Maybe it is because the potential problems are mostly underground. Just because they are unseen should not mean that you should postpone addressing them. In areas where irrigation is necessary, the problems will be sooner rather than later.

Some years back, when we were contemplating taking over the famous "Russian Farm in Egypt," drainage and salinity problems were quite evident. With literally hundreds of millions of dollars provided for the irrigation system, not one dollar was spent on drainage! The farm was on the east side of the Cairo-to-Alexandria highway and sloped from the highway down to the Nile. As one progressed from the highway to the river, it was evident that the quality of the citrus trees deteriorated as one got closer to the Nile. Their experts blamed the poor quality on frost, mites—everything but drainage. It took time and persuasion to convince the ministers of agriculture and irrigation that drainage was the culprit. Fortunately, we had some powerful help in Dr. Kamal Stino, Dr. Osman Badran and Dr. Hassan Baghdadi, all former cabinet ministers, highly intelligent and educated, with Ph.Ds from the University of California. With their help and influence, the problem was addressed. We had designed a system and created a test plot with the proper drainage ditches, and underground pipes, and the results were almost immediately evident. This precipitated a request for drainage funds from the international lending agencies. Unfortunately, politics intervened—they were perhaps learning the art of politics from Washington—or they felt their constituents would not believe the need was real and justified because the "equipment" basically was underground and could not be seen. But in the end, reason, good sense and technical expertise prevailed.

In a similar vein, the attitude of out-of-sight, out-of-mind is somewhat prevalent in the states. But be forewarned, if you don't assess your potential drainage problems and use good management practices, your yields will gradually decline. Eventually, poor drainage may result in the death of your trees. Then only salt tolerant species such as barley and oats become your crop!

Therefore, make sure your land and irrigation water are satisfactory for good pecan production. Have your soil and water analyzed, check your soil profile for the possibility of hardpans, etc., and make sure your soil texture is satisfactory so its permeability is not impaired. In irrigated areas, ensure that sodium and chloride are not a potential problem. If the SAR (sodium absorption ratio) of the soil or water is above 3.0, check with a specialist for further input. Site and soil selection are your best defense for salinity problems and even good sites may need corrective action. With irrigation becoming more widespread as a management tool, having a good site with a workable and effective salinity management program will go a long way towards encouraging good nut production. Don't ignore it!

Insect and Disease Control: Insect and disease control can be a major production problem with pecans. Know the life history of the causal agent, and be aware of the phenological development of the tree so that you can take advantage of the most opportune time to maximize pest control. You will thereby prevent damage to the tree and/or its nuts. Knowledge, observation and timing are important.

Most diseases and insects affecting pecans can be controlled by:
>   1) a regular spray program;
>   2) good sanitation practices;
>   3) resistant or tolerant varieties and
>   4) any combination of the foregoing.

Current and specific control measures for both insects and diseases on pecans are available from the state agricultural extension service.

Your program should be designed to be biologically effective, ecologically sound and cost effective for market conditions and your specific grove.

The Major Insect Pests that Affect Pecans

There are many insects that feed on the leaves, buds and nuts of pecan trees. Damage by these insects can reduce the marketability of the nuts and reduce tree vigor. It is important to identify and survey insect populations so serious damage is prevented. The following list describes the most common insect pests.

Pecan Weevil: These destructive insects are called snout beetles and usually can be found wherever pecans are grown. They are of economic importance to pecan growers because they damage the marketable product—the nut. The life cycle of the pecan weevil begins in the latter part of the summer when the light-brown adults, one-half to three-fourth inches long, emerge. They lay their eggs in the nut by using their long beaks to make a puncture through the shucks and shells. The white larvae (legless grubs), hatch from eggs, feed on the kernels and eventually exit the shell through circular holes. They then drop to and enter the soil, where they pupate either the same or second year and emerge as adults.

Pecan Nut Casebearer: This insect is potentially very damaging to the pecan tree because the first generation larvae feed on buds and terminal growth. The life cycle begins when the overwintered larvae or worms, about one-half inch long, with greenish bodies and brown heads, emerge from their cocoons in early spring or bud break. They begin feeding on buds, but then move out to terminal shoots and burrow into the centers. Then, they pupate in the stem or crawl down the limb and pupate on the tree. In several days, the adult moths spring forth, mate and lay their eggs on the blossom end of the nut. These eggs hatch and the larvae usually feed initially on an adjacent bud, but then, by biological programming or coincidence, on a newly formed nut. The larvae pupate in the last nuts they hollow out and emerge as adult moths in approximately ten days to start the second generation. This cycle repeats itself as long as weather permits.

Hickory Shuckworm: This insect can be a late season problem because it burrows into the soft, green shuck or husk and disrupts normal kernel development. The life cycle begins in spring when the larvae pupate in overwintered shucks. Shortly thereafter adult moths emerge and deposit eggs on pecan buds of early fruiting varieties or other hosts such as hickory and phylloxera galls. The eggs hatch and the larvae burrow into the buds and feed for two to three weeks. Then pupation occurs and the adult moth repeats the cycle by laying its eggs on the now available pecan shuck. The cycle is repeated several times during the growing season. The fully grown larvae overwinter in infested pecan shucks.

Pecan Aphids: Aphids are small, sucking insects that are an annual problem on most pecan trees. There are two kinds that attack pecans; the black pecan aphid and the black margined aphid. Both insects suck juices from the leaves and secrete honeydew. However, the black pecan aphid, even in low numbers, is generally considered more destructive because it injects a toxin into the leaves that causes yellow spots, that ultimately turn brown. This causes premature defoliation and lowers the productivity of the tree. The black margined aphid doesn't cause the yellow and brown spots on the leaves, but heavy infestations will cause premature defoliation which affects the nut crop.

The honeydew that both of these insects secrete causes indirect damage. The sweet, sticky, syrup-like honeydew coats the leaves and reduces their ability to function properly. The honeydew also supports a black mold, which reduces the photosynthetic capacity of the leaves and is a source of contamination in packaged nuts.

Multiple generations (a mild understatement), are the rule for both aphids and they overwinter as eggs on twigs and bark of infested trees. An interesting phenomena is that all summer forms of the insect are female and reproduce without mating.

Fall Webworm: These wooly caterpillars are more of an unsightly nuisance pest than a destructive one. However, they do cause defoliation and heavy populations can weaken trees. The life cycle begins in spring when adult white moths emerge from overwintered cocoons and deposit their eggs, in masses, on the underside of pecan leaves and other hosts. The eggs hatch producing one-inch long caterpillars that create a web or nest over the leaves. Inside the web, the worms feed, and in four to six weeks, they leave the web and crawl down the tree to pupate. The adult moths emerge in late summer and begin the cycle over again for the second and most destructive generation. When the last crop of worms mature in late fall, they drop to the ground, spin their cocoons and overwinter as protected pupae in cracks in the soil or under leaves.

Major Diseases of Pecans

Pecans are affected by fungi, bacteria and plant parasitic nematodes. Their occurrence, and the degree and magnitude of their damage, is greatly influenced by climatic conditions inherent in the geographical area where susceptible trees are grown. Wet, humid weather is conducive to the spread of disease. Because the Western irrigated area is characterized by a high degree of sunshine, low humidity and little rainfall, this area is not unduly affected by most of the pecan diseases. Conversely, the high temperatures and frequent irrigations are conducive to high nematode populations.

Scab: Scab is probably the most serious of pecan diseases. It is distinguished by round or irregular olive-brown to black spots on leaves, young twigs and nuts. The leaf lesions vary from a barely discernible dot, to one which is one-fourth inch or more in diameter. These lesions commonly occur on the undersides of the leaves, both inter- and intraveinally, and on the petioles. Nut lesions first appear as a slightly raised spot, but later become concave. These spots will usually enlarge, and if there are many, the nuts will drop prematurely. Twig lesions develop during late summer or early fall and serve to carry the organism through the winter.

This disease can be mistaken for vein spot, but with scab the lesions are randomly distributed over the leaf versus leaf spot where the elongated lesions are located along the veins.

Scab is probably the most important factor in the screening process for new varieties as it largely determines the geographical area of usefulness for the variety.

Liver Spot: This fungus disease is found primarily in the Deep South; its name reflects the color of the lesion. The disease first appears in late spring as clearly defined, dark reddish-brown circular spots on the lower leaf surface, mainly along each side of the midvein. While severely infected leaves may drop, it seldom results in an economic loss.

Vein Spot: This fungus disease is prevalent primarily in the southern Mississippi River region. It affects only leaves, causing lesions to form on the veins or stems. The lesions on lateral veins are usually less than one-fourth inch in diameter. The midrib lesions sometimes extend from the base to the apex of the leaflet. The spots are dark brown to black in the final stage and heavy infections result in defoliation.

Vein spot can be confused with scab, but with this disease, the lesions almost always occur along the veins and they are more elongated in shape.

Leaf Blotch: Leaf blotch is a fungus disease caused by a weak pathogen. The disease manifests itself as olive-green, velvety tufts in early summer on the underside of mature leaves. Later, yellow lesions appear on the upper surface. The fungus produces black spores on the under-surface of the leaves about midsummer. In due course, more infection sites form and the fruiting structures unite, giving the leaves a black, shiny, blotched appearance. The early symptoms and signs of the disease may be confused with downy spot but as the lesions age the similarity lessens.

Bunch Disease: This disease is distinguished by an overabundance of willowy stem shoots that gives a bushy appearance to the tree. The disease, thought to be caused by a mycoplasm-like organism, appears to be infectious as it is thought to spread from tree to tree.

The symptoms are more conspicuous in spring and early summer because leaves and twigs develop earlier and are more prolific than those of unaffected branches. Ultimately, affected trees may look quite unusual—their main branches bunched with thick broomy sucker growth. On such trees, many leaflets die and fall in late summer. Some symptoms may be mistaken for pecan rosette, but the latter can be controlled with zinc compounds as described under Fertilization, while bunch disease cannot.

Crown Gall: Crown gall is a bacterial disease which causes galls or tumor-like aberrations on the roots or the base of the trunk of pecan trees. The disease is found in many soils, but can enter the plant only through wounds in the roots or bark. The disease gradually weakens the tree and young infected trees may die. Avoid planting new trees in soil where diseased plants were grown unless you fumigate first. Carefully inspect the planting stock. Nursery trees that have suspicious swellings near the crown or graft union or on lateral roots should be rejected.

Physiological Disorders

The following are several physiological disorders that may influence the productive capacity of your pecan grove.

Pecan Rosette: This disorder is caused by a zinc deficiency and occurs most commonly on calcareous alkaline soils. Symptoms are usually first noticed the second or third year after transplanting. The first symptom is the appearance of small, narrow leaves that are yellow and mottled. Reddish-brown areas or perforations often appear between the veins on older leaves. Internodes become shortened and an excess of small branches is formed giving the foliage a rosette appearance. In the final stages of the disorder, the shoots die back from the tips. Usually, the die-back is confined to the current year's growth, but it sometimes extends to older branches of considerable size. Seriously affected pecan trees rarely bear nuts, and the nuts that are formed are usually small and poorly filled. Some symptoms resemble crown gall, but pecan rosette can usually be corrected with foliar applications of zinc; crown gall cannot.

Pecan Die-Back: This disorder often occurs in areas where one or more of these conditions exist: hardpan layers, caliche soils, high salt, and poor drainage. Very often trees planted under these conditions make adequate growth for a few years after they are transplanted, but then, because of the poor soil condition, start dying back from the tips in later years.

There is no easy solution to this problem in heavy soils with poor drainage. A caliche or hardpan layer can be detected and somewhat broken up by deep root plowing. Die-back sometimes occurs because of a lack of water, particularly in light, sandy soils during the winter months. Moisture condition of the soil around the tree should be monitored throughout the entire year.

Winter Injury: This potential problem is usually the result of an interaction between the weather and management practices. The bark on a winter-injured tree appears sunken and is cracked where it meets the growing tissue. Healthy trees in a proper dormant condition can withstand low temperatures. However, if the tree makes excessive vegetative growth late into the fall, the proper hardening of tissue does not take place.

Plants overfed with high-nitrogen fertilizer and those receiving heavy fall irrigations are most likely to become injured. Soil applications of fertilizer, especially nitrogen, should be made in the winter, early spring or as recommended by your agricultural extension service. Reduce or halt the number of irrigations in September. After the trees become dormant, apply a heavy irrigation to provide a favorable environment for the roots during the winter.

Sunscald: This injury can be serious with newly transplanted nursery trees because they are especially susceptible to sunscald. The symptoms are dead or cankerous areas which usually appear on the southwest side of the trunk or on the upper surfaces of large branches. Young trees can be protected by wrapping with burlap strips or aluminum foil, painting the trunk with a white latex paint or employing the "trashy trunk" method of tree establishment and pruning.

Weed Control

Grass and weed competition can be easily classified as the most widespread single factor that reduces tree growth and lowers pecan yields and quality. While it is true that losses from pecan insects and diseases are sizeable, these losses vary from year to year and in different geographical locations. Grass and weeds thrive in all areas where pecans are grown. They are consistent competitors for water and nutrients needed for maximum tree growth, precocity and production. This is particularly true for young groves. Weeds and grass need to be removed under the tree canopy. In older groves, use a relatively non-competing-type sod for efficient management and harvesting operations.

An effective weed-control program is needed for commercial pecan groves in all pecan growing areas. The objectives of the program should be to: lower competition for water and nutrients, enhance harvesting operations, prevent soil erosion, and assist in the biological control of insects and diseases. These may be accomplished by cultivation, mowing or chemical means, or a combination of the three. For up-to-date specific recommendations see your state agricultural extension agent.

Pruning

The general purpose of all pruning is to increase yields, improve quality and reduce production costs. With the advent of close spacings, the need to control tree size becomes of paramount importance. Such plantings require varieties that are adaptable to small-tree culture.

The modern trend in pecan culture is toward heavier and more consistent pruning and tree thinning, both in young and mature trees. The precocious and fruitful new varieties respond more quickly and favorably to this than most of the older varieties, but even with the latter, consistent thinning out and more attention to light penetration seems effective and desirable throughout the bearing life of the trees.

Pruning and training of young trees during their pre-production years have been discussed previously. Pruning in bearing years is a relatively new production practice and advancements in this field are rapidly developing. Currently, hedging, pollarding, pole pruning and selective limb removal are all practiced to some extent.

In high-density plantings, besides tree removal, two types of pruning are employed. The first method is to "pancake" every other tree in the row. This is done by cutting the trees "cross row," two to four feet wide, straight up and down. This removes limbs from both sides of one tree, keeping it from overlapping with the next tree. With this type of pruning, every other tree will need to be removed at some future date when the remaining trees begin to overlap.

The other type of mechanical pruning is "hedging" or "hedge-row" pruning. This involves running the pruning equipment with the rows, as opposed to across the rows as in "pancaking." With this concept, all trees are pruned and all trees may remain in the grove.

It is considered essential to thin the trees when the branches first touch. Our suggestion, as in the cattle business, is to look, listen, investigate and experiment. But keep an open and intellectually honest mind.

Harvesting

The most costly single item in pecan production is the harvesting operation. Pecans must be harvested as soon as possible after they mature to prevent loss from wildlife. In the past, bamboo poles were used to flail pecans to the ground and then the nuts were picked up by hand. Today, with the increasing sophistication of mechanical shaking and harvesting equipment, coupled with good orchard floor management, you are able to harvest the crop mechanically in an efficient and economical manner. The main advantages of mechanical harvesting are:

1) a reduction in costly and scarce hand labor;
2) an increase in the rate of harvest;
3) an improvement in harvesting efficiency and
4) a reduction in the harvesting cost (in most cases).

Shakers: There are many excellent pecan tree-shakers available. These range in price from homemade models costing almost nil, to expensive self-propelled hydraulic models priced between $50,000 and $75,000 in 1998. If not self-propelled, a tractor of 50-90 HP will be needed depending on the model of the shaker.

Sweepers: Used to windrow pecans, the sweepers in 1998 cost between $10,000 and $30,000.

Harvesters: There is still a lot of research being conducted to determine a satisfactory method to get or keep the pecans off the ground. There are several harvesting machines on the market, but no single machine has proven adaptable to all pecan-growing conditions. Pecan harvesters are available in several styles: self-propelled, tractor-mounted or PTO-assisted models. Under good grove management conditions and depending on tree density and yield per tree, they can harvest ten to twenty acres per day.

The performance of all harvesters is greatly improved by cleaning and preparing the grove floor in advance of the harvest. The use of side-delivery rakes or mechanical sweepers to windrow the pecans speeds the harvest operation. Inasmuch as mechanical harvesters cannot distinguish between pecans and foreign material similar in size and shape, their use necessitates the use of a nut-cleaning machine to put the pecans into marketable condition. Cleaning machines have a capacity of 5,000 to 10,000 pounds per day for portable units to upwards of 10,000 pounds per hour for complete cleaning plants.

You can see the different kinds of machinery at your state pecan association meeting. Usually a full line of equipment and accessories will be on display, with technical assistance available.

Storage

Pecans can be maintained in a fresh condition until they are consumed if they are properly handled and stored. But, a high quality kernel is essential for pecans going into storage. Storage does not improve pecan quality. At best it maintains the quality of the nut at the time it was put in storage. With both in-shell and shelled pecans, the general rule is that the lower the storage temperature, the longer the storage life of the pecan. Pecans stored at zero degrees Fahrenheit are usually edible for up to twenty-four months.

Freshly harvested pecans, when well cured contain about 9–12 percent protein, 10 percent carbohydrate, 65–75 percent oil, 3 percent water, and 2 percent ash made up of various mineral elements. Pecan oil is about 93 percent unsaturated. However, since the oil content is high, rancidity development at warm temperatures is more noticeable than in most other nuts. Incidentally, the oil in pecans is largely unsaturated oleic and linoleic acid, thus considered more healthful.

Marketing

In the United States, pecans are marketed by approximately eighty firms located throughout the pecan belt from North Carolina to New Mexico and in St. Louis, Chicago and Pittsburgh. The crop is sold in two general categories, in-shell and shelled. The marketing trend is for shelled nuts. In fact, a recent USDA survey showed that 94 percent of the pecans that entered commercial channels were shelled. The primary user of shelled pecans was the baking industry, accounting for 36 percent of the total. Sales via retail packages accounted for 24 percent, while confectioners used 19 percent and ice cream manufacturers utilized 6 percent of the total. The rest was used by salters, repackers and mail-order gift packers.

Prices received by producers or ranchers for pecans are affected by quality, the percent kernel, the size of the domestic crop and by supplies of competing nuts. During the 1990s grower prices for improved varieties averaged between $0.62 and $1.57 per pound.

Quality and percent of edible kernel are the most important ingredients the grower can control that determine the actual price. However, high-quality nuts always command a premium that is above the average. In recent years shellers have become more amenable to thinking in terms of paying in relation to the percent of kernel. So the price-quality relationship has become more important. New varieties, with an inherent high percentage of kernel and grown under good management, offer the best bet for the producer to obtain premium prices.

Economics of Production

The example and economics discussed in this section refer solely to a typical grove planted and maintained in an intensive manner in the western irrigated pecan-producing area.

The use of new precocious and prolific varieties in high-density plantings, under irrigated conditions has brought about radical improvement in the economics of pecan production. Not only is the preproduction interval shortened, but yields during the bearing years are significantly increased. These increases in yield usually overcome the added expense connected with intensified culture techniques. However, many of these techniques are coming under increased scrutiny because of some detrimental aspects to the longterm vitality of the grove.

Projected per Acre Yield, Income and Cash Expenses for a Pecan Grove Planted and Managed in an Intensive Manner in the Western Irrigated Area

	Years After Transplanting				
	4	5	6	7-11	12-20
Yield/acre, lbs.	400	800	1,200	1,400	1,600
Cash value @ $1.20/lb	$480	$960	$1,440	$1,680	$1,920
Production expense	-300	-400	-400	-450	-500
Harvesting expense*	-60	-120	-180	-210	-240
Net cash income	$120	$440	$860	$1,020	$1,180

* Harvesting expense based on fifteen cents per pound.

It takes at least four years to bring a new pecan grove into commercial production and grove establishment and preproduction costs, excluding land value, will probably approach $2,000 per acre. Yields, expenses and income, that would be expected from a typical grove planted with high-producing, precocious varieties, managed in an intensive manner, are given above. These projections are based on average yields; trees grown under poorer or better intensified conditions would be expected to produce lower to higher yields, respectively. Additionally, a decrease or increase in the value of pecans would be reflected in a lower or higher net cash income for the crop.

We want to point out that many producers rarely make a profit. In fact, some may never because of natural limitations, poor management or poor luck. Furthermore, there are few, if any, tax benefits, so your effort must be for the love of the pecan or your desire to beat the odds.

We hope this brief discussion has piqued your interest in the pecan industry and, because our experience is in Texas, most of our information has been gleaned from Texas A & M sources. There are many pecan growers, in other states, who have made contributions to this industry. We encourage you to contact your county agricultural extension agent or the state extension horticulturist, usually located at your state agricultural or land grant institution. In addition, The Texas Pecan Growers Association publishes *Pecan South,* a very informative journal, and distributes the Texas Agricultural Extension Service's *Texas Pecan Handbook.* The handbook is a very useful and detailed guide, which is updated yearly. Both may be obtained from TPGA, Drawer CC, College Station, TX, 77841.

Part Four:

Winding Down

Chapter 10

The Transfer of the Ranch

General Concepts

Sooner or later the time will come for an orderly transfer of the ranch, either by outright sale or by a non-sale transfer to family members or a trust. It is important to reiterate the need for an experienced real estate attorney and ranch estate/tax expert. Many of the structural matters relating to transfer were, hopefully, well thought out at the time of purchase. Remember, you need an over-all estate plan that also provides adequate liquidity to the estate. Otherwise, your will and estate plan may not be effectively satisfied. And don't forget to consider transferring property during life—at least you will know where it is going and will share the appreciation with the recipient!

If the transfer is going to be by sale, we strongly recommend you enlist the aid of an experienced real estate agent. Use those who are experienced in the farm and ranch area of the business.

Agents spend time and money on specialized advertising, and will network in farm and ranch circles. Their knowledge and familiarity with technical farm and ranch matters will also help you sell the ranch. Give them an exclusive listing for at least a year so they will invest in advertising to market your ranch. The fees normally run from 5 to 10 percent of the gross sale price of the property. Also enlist their knowledge in pricing the ranch properly—if you want it sold. Price it accordingly. You know the old saying, "A bird in hand is worth many flitting around," or something like that. Expensive farm and ranch real estate seems to attract the many flitting kooks of the world, so let an experienced land agent assist you.

To facilitate matters related to the sale try to compile all the material listed on the following checklist. It will help you to talk intelligently with your real estate broker and will also help protect you in any potential disagreement with the buyer, then or downstream. Disclosure, per se, helps in building confidence and ultimately in the sale of the property.

A Checklist for Marketing the Property

✓ Present legal owner—name, address, phone, fax
✓ Copy of deed into present owner
✓ Copy of latest survey with metes and bounds, rights, easements, etc.
✓ Copy of last title policy
✓ List of outstanding notes, if any
✓ Surface leases, oil and gas leases, right of way easements, hunting leases, deed restrictions, etc.
✓ Aerial photo of property
✓ Flood plain map and soil survey of property
✓ Topographic map of property
✓ Room measurements of home and other ranch buildings
✓ Description and specifications of all improvements—barns, houses, fences, pastures, grasses, water source.
✓ Name of local school district and location of office
✓ Description of all taxing authorities—rates and amounts
✓ Tax (ownership) map from county appraisal district office

- ✓ Measured distances from nearest towns for supplies
- ✓ Details of roads to property
- ✓ Recent animal capacities and crop production figures
- ✓ Summary of positive features—five sales points to make to a buyer
- ✓ Exclusive listing agreement
- ✓ Executed house disclosure forms, such as condition report, lead paint presence, Environmental Protection Agency reports, termite inspection report, etc.

Good luck, and may your ranching experiences be pleasant and profitable ones.

Appendix 1

Beef Cattle Breeders Associations

Angus
American Angus Association
3201 Frederick Boulevard
St. Joseph, MO 64506
Tel: 816-383-5100; Fax: 816-233-9703

Beefmaster
Beefmaster Breeders United
6800 Park Ten Blvd. Suite 290 West
San Antonio, TX 78213
Tel: 210-732-3132; Fax: 210-732-7711

Belgian Blue
American Belgian Blue Breeders, Inc.
P.O. Box 34663
N. Kansas City, MO 64116
Tel: 816-471-2583; Fax: 816-421-1991

Blonde d'Aquitaine
American Blonde d'Aquitaine Ass'n
P.O. Box 12341
Kansas City, MO 64116
Tel: 816-421-1305; Fax: 816-421-1991

Braford
United Braford Breeders
422 East Main, Suite 218
Nacogdoches, TX 75961
Tel: 409-569-8200; Fax: 409-569-9556

Brahman
American Brahman Breeders Ass'n
1313 La Concha Lane
Houston, TX 77054-1890
Tel: 713-795-4444; Fax: 713-795-4450

Brangus
International Brangus Breeders Ass'n
P.O. Box 696020
San Antonio, TX 78269-6020
Tel: 210-696-8231; Fax: 210-696-8718

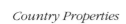

Braunvieh	The Braunvieh Association of America P.O. Box 6396 Lincoln, NE 68506 Tel: 402-421-2960; Fax: 402-421-2994
Charolais	American-International Charolais Ass'n P.O. Box 20247 Kansas City, MO 64195 Tel: 816-464-5977; Fax: 816-464-5759
Chianina	American Chianina Association P.O. Box 890 Platte City, MO 64079 Tel: 816-431-2808; Fax: 816-431-5381
Gelbvieh	American Gelbvieh Association 10900 Dover Street Westminster, CO 80021-3993 Tel: 303-465-2333; Fax: 303-465-2339
Hereford	The American Hereford Association 1501 Wyandotte Street Kansas City, MO 64101 Tel: 816-842-3757; Fax: 816-842-6931
Limousin	North American Limousin Foundation P.O. Box 4467 7383 S. Alton Way Englewood, CO 80155 Tel: 303-220-1693; Fax: 303-220-1884
Maine-Anjou	American Maine-Anjou Association 760 Livestock Exchange Building Kansas City, MO 64102 Tel: 816-474-9555; Fax: 816-474-9556
Marchigiana	Marky Cattle Association Box 198 Walton, KS 67151-0198
Murray Grey	American Murray Grey Association P.O. Box 34590 N. Kansas City, MO 64116-0990 Tel: 816-421-1994; Fax: 816-421-1991

Normande	North American Normande Ass'n 11538 Spudville Road Hibbing, MN 55746 Tel: 218-262-1933
Piedmontese	Piedmontese Ass'n of the United States 108 Livestock Exchange Building 4701 Marion Street Denver, CO 80216 Tel: 303-295-7287; Fax: 303-295-7935
Pinzgauer	American Pinzgauer Association 21555 S.R. 698 Jenera, OH 45841 1-800-914-9883
Polled Hereford	The American Hereford Association 1501 Wyandotte Street Kansas City, MO 64101 Tel: 816-842-3757; Fax: 816-842-6931
Red Angus	Red Angus Association 4201 I-35 North Denton, TX 76207-3415 Tel: 817-387-3502; Fax: 817-383-4036
Red Brangus	American Red Brangus Association 3995 East Hwy. 290 Dripping Springs, TX 78620-4205 Tel: 512-858-7285; Fax: 512-858-7084
Red Poll	American Red Poll Association P.O. Box 147 Bethany, MO 64424 Tel: 660-425-7318; Fax: 660-425-8374
Romagnola	American Romagnola Association 2000 Flagstone Road Reno, NV 89510 Tel: 775-475-2333; Fax: 775-475-2697
Salers	American Salers Association 7383 South Alton Way, Suite 103 Englewood, CO 80112 Tel: 303-770-9292; Fax: 303-770-9302

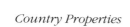

Salorn	International Salorn Association P.O. Box 198 Granby, MO 64844-0198 Tel: 417-472-7133
Santa Gertrudis	Santa Gertrudis Breeders International Box 1257 Kingsville, TX 78364-1257 Tel: 512-592-9357; Fax: 512-592-8572
Senepol	Senepol Cattle Breeders Association P.O. Box 901594 Kansas City, MO 64190-1594 Tel: 800-736-3765
Shorthorn	American Shorthorn Association 8288 Hascall Street Omaha, NE 68124 Tel: 402-393-7200; Fax: 402-393-7203
Simbrah	American Simmental Association 1 Simmental Way Bozeman, MT 59715-9990 Tel: 406-587-4531; Fax: 406-587-9301
Simmental	American Simmental Association 1 Simmental Way Bozeman, MT 59715-9990 Tel: 406-587-4531; Fax: 406-587-9301
Texas Longhorn	Texas Longhorn Breeders Ass'n of America 2315 N. Main Street, Suite 402 Fort Worth, TX 76106 Tel: 817-625-6241; Fax: 817-625-1388
Wagyu	American Wagyu Association P.O. Box 4071 Bryan, TX 77805 Tel: 409-260-0300

Selected References

After a Hundred Years: Yearbook of Agriculture. Washington, D.C.: USDA, 1962.

Animal Diseases: Yearbook of Agriculture. Washington, D.C.: USDA, 1956.

Ashton, F.M. & Monaco, T.J. *Weed Science: Principles and Practices*. New York, N.Y.: John Wiley, 1991.

Bagby, J.R. *Real Estate Financing Desk Book*. Englewood Cliffs, N.J.: Institute for Business Planning, 1977.

Barnes, R.F., Miller, D.A. and Nelson, C.J. *Forages: An Introduction to Grassland Agricultures*. Ames, Iowa: Iowa Sate University Press, 1995.

Beard, T. and Arndt, J. *The Cowboy Book*. Salt Lake City, Utah: Peregrine, 1992.

Black, C.A. *Soil Fertility, Evaluation and Control*. Boca Raton, Fla: CRC Press, 1993.

Bray, C.I. and Schmidt, G.A. *Practical Activities in Animal Husbandry*. New York, N.Y.: Appleton-Century, 1926.

Briggs, H.M. *Modern Breeder of Livestock*. New York, N.Y.: The MacMillan Co., 1980.

Brison, F.R. *Pecan Culture*. Austin, Texas: Capital Printing, 1974.

Buol, S.W., Hole, F.D. and McCracken, R.J. *Soil Genesis and Classification*. Ames, Iowa: Iowa State University, 1988.

Darwin, C. *The Origin of Species*. London and New York: J.M. Dent and E.P. Dutton, 1928 and 1958.

DeGraff, H. and Haystead, L. *The Business of Farming*. Norman, Okla. : University of Oklahoma Press, 1948.

Diseases of Cattle: Special Report. Washington, D.C.: USDA.

Drainage of Agricultural Land. Port Washington, N.Y: Water Information Center, 1973.

Ensminger, M.E. *The Stockman's Handbook*. Danville, Ill.: Interstate Publishers, 1992.

Forth, H.D. and Ellis, B.G. *Soil Fertility*. New York: John Wiley, 1988.

Gustafson, A.F. Hardenburg, E.V., Smith, E.Y. and McCay, J.B. *Land for the Family—A Guide to Country Living.* Ithaca, N.Y.: Comstock Publishing Co., Inc., 1947.

Harl, N.E. *Farm Estate & Business Planning.* Skokie, Ill.: Century Communications, 1984.

Harris, J.C. and Friedman, J.P. *Barron's Real Estate Handbook,* Hauppauge, N.Y.: Barron's Educational Series, Inc., 1997.

Hart, V.B, Bond, M.C. & Cunningham, L.C. *Farm Management and Marketing.* New York, N.Y.: John Wiley, 1942.

Harwood, B. *New York Real Estate.* Upper Saddle River, N.J.: Reston Publishing, 1997.

Hatch, S.L. and Pluhar, J. *Texas Range Plants.* College Station, Texas: Texas A&M University Press, 1995.

Isely, D. *Weed Identification and Control.* Ames, Iowa: ISU Press, 1960.

Jacobus, C.J., and Harwood, B. *Texas Real Estate.* Englewood Cliffs, N.J.: Prentice-Hall Career & Technology, 1995.

Jaffe, A..J. and Sirmans,C.F. *Fundamentals of Real Estate Investment.* Englewood Cliffs, N.J.: Prentice-Hall, 1995.

Jaynes, R.A.. *Handbook of North American Nut Trees.* Knoxville, Tenn.: Northern Nut Growers Association, 1969.

Kains, N.G. *Five Acres and Independence.* New York, N.Y.: Dover Publishing, 1973.

Klingman, G.C., Ashton, F.M. and Noordhoff, L.J. *Weed Science: Principles and Practices.* New York, N.Y.: John Wiley, 1975.

Kohls, R.L. and Uhl, J.N. *Marketing of Agricultural Products.* New York, N.Y.: Macmillan, 1998.

Land: 1958 Yearbook of Agriculture. Washington, D.C.: USDA, 1958.

"Land—Buying into the Dream." (1997, February). *Worth* magazine.

Lea, T. *The King Ranch.* Boston, Mass.: Little, Brown, 1957.

Living on a Few Acres: Yearbook of Agriculture. Washington, D.C.: USDA, 1978.

Lorenz, O.A., and Maynard, D.N. *Knott's Handbook for Vegetable Growers.* New York, N.Y.: John Wiley, 1988.

Lush, R.H. *Pasture Production and Management.* New York, N.Y.: Blakiston, 1952.

Matthews, G.A. *Pesticide Application Methods.* New York, N.Y.: John Wiley, 1992.

Montgomery, E.G. *Productive Farm Crops.* Philadelphia, Pa.: J.B. Lippincott, 1928.

Morrison, F.B. *Feeds and Feeding* . Clinton, Iowa. Morrison Publishing Co., 1959.

Murray, W.G., Harris, D.G., Miller, G.A., and Thompson, N.S. *Farm Appraisal and Valuation*. Ames, Iowa: Iowa State, 1983.

Newmann, A.L. *Beef Cattle*, New York, N.Y.: John Wiley and Sons, 1977.

Nixon, J. *Cowboy Marketing*. Karnes City, Texas: Nixon, 1995.

Ogilvy, D. *Ogilvy on Advertising*. New York, N.Y.: Vintage Books, 1985.

O'Mary, C.C. and Dyer, I.A. *Commercial Beef Cattle Production*. Philadelphia, Pa.: Lea & F, 1978.

Oppenheimer, H.L. *Cowboy Arithmetic*. Danville, Ill.: Interstate, 1985.

Ornduff, D.R. *The Hereford in America*. Kansas City, Mo.: Ornduff, 1969.

Outdoors, USA: Yearbook of Agriculture. Washington, D.C.: USDA, 1967.

Ryugo, K. *Fruit Culture: Its Science and Art*. New York, N.Y.: John Wiley, 1988.

Sanders, A.H. *Shorthorn Cattle*. Chicago, Ill.: Sanders, 1981.

Sher, L and Sher, C. *Finding and Buying Your Place in the Country*. Chicago, Ill.: Dearborn Financial Publishing, 1996.

Singer, M.J. and Munns, D.N. *Soils: An Introduction*. Upper Saddle River, N.J.: Prentice-Hall, 1996.

Sirmans, C.F. *Real Estate Finance*. New York, N.Y.: McGraw-Hill, 1989.

Texas Pecan Handbook. College Station, Texas: Texas A&M University, 1997.

Towne, C.W. and Wentworth, E.N. *Cattle & Men*. Norman, Okla.: University of Oklahoma Press, 1955.

Tyson, E. and Brown, R. *House Selling for Dummies*. Foster City, Calif.: IDG Books Worldwide, 1997.

Vaughan, H.W. *Types and Market Classes of Livestock*. Columbus, Ohio: College Book, 1942.

Williams, J.W. *The Big Ranch Country*. Burnet, Texas: Nortex Press, 1971.

Yearbook of the Department of Agriculture. (1895). Washington, D.C.: USDA, 1895.

Glossary

acre—A measure of land in any shape equal to 43,560 square feet. Equal to 4,047 square meters or 0.40 hectares.

ad valorem taxes—Taxes based upon the value of the property.

A.I.—Artificial insemination or the impregnation of a cow or heifer by the artificial introduction of semen.

alkaline soil—Soil which has a pH greater than 7.0.

aquifer—A natural underground reservoir of water into which wells may be drilled.

back forty—A metaphor for a secluded, secretive or remote portion of a farm or ranch.

beef type—An ideal or visual standard of perfection that contributes to a beef animal's usefulness as a meat animal, such as excellent conformation and a great width and depth of body.

biochemical pathways—The routes that substances found in the living animal take or undergo during its life.

bottom line—To the lowest line of an earnings report where net profits are shown. In slang usage, may refer to the most important factor or meaning.

bred-back cow—A cow that has been successfully bred after calving.

breed association—An association that promotes the breed and maintains the registration book for its registered cattle.

breeding cattle—Cattle that are of proper age, high standard and usefulness in perpetuating or improving their likeness.

brisket—A specific frontal area of a beef animal commonly identified in the breast area.

British breeds—Usually intended to mean Angus, Hereford and Shorthorn.

bump-type gate—A gate in a ranch fence, developed by the King Ranch and the former Humble Oil and Refining Co., that opens when bumped by the front of a car or truck.

calf—An unbred cow or bull under one year of age.

cancer eye—A disorder in cattle thought to be inherited with greater frequency in cattle with white hair and unpigmented skin on the eyelids.

carcass grade—A carcass evaluation based on merit and determined by the quality or eating characteristics of the meat and the proportion of lean meat.

carcass-value basis—A pricing system for cattle based on the value of the carcass to the beef processor (packer).

carry-over basis—A provision under tax laws that allows the application of deductions and credits of one taxable year, which cannot be used to reduce tax liability in that year, to tax liabilities in subsequent years.

carrying capacity—A cattleman's term that refers to the number of cow/calf units that an acre of pasture will support.

cash flow—An accounting term describing the positive or negative effect on cash generated from operations. From a practical standpoint, it is computed as the total net income plus depreciation accruals and adjusted for other sources and applications of funds.

check valve—A valve in a piping system that prevents flow reversal. The energy for opening and closing the valve comes entirely from the dynamic forces of the flowing liquid.

clay or clayey types—A classification of soil referring to topsoils that have a high proportion of fine-textured soil particles, commonly called heavy soils.

clayey loam—A soil classification in which the aggregate soil particle distribution is midway between extreme smallness (silt) and extreme size (sand). The loam group is generally considered a better agricultural soil.

cloning—A process whereby the progeny or descendants are descended asexually from a single common ancestor and are genetically identical to one another.

commercial herd—A herd of cattle that probably is not registered under a breed association's criteria, but may be, and is used to produce grade cattle for the commercial market.

community property—A legal term, in certain states, that refers to property accumulated through joint efforts and owned equally by a husband and wife.

conformation score—A subjective rating of conformation characteristics of a live beef animal that are based on skeletal soundness and carcass desirability.

contour lines—A line on a topographical or contour map that connects all points of the same elevation or depth of a particular parcel of land.

contour map—A map that represents the elevations or depths of a specific area of land.

cow—A mature, female beef animal.

cow efficiency—A colloquial term to describe the maternal traits of a productive female that ensures the production of a calf every year and her ability to wean it to a heavy weight.

cow/calf unit—The combination of mother cow and suckling calf.

CPA—Certified public accountant.

crest—In beef cattle refers to the ridge of the neck.

crossbreeding—The interbreeding of different breeds of livestock resulting in hybrids.

dam—The female parent of a calf or offspring.

deed of trust—An instrument used to transfer legal title of property from the owner to a trustee so that the trustee may hold the title as security for the performance of certain obligations, then reconveyed to the owner or its transferee upon satisfaction of those obligations, such as payment in full of a mortgage.

discounted cash flow—A measure of the present value of a future income stream generated by a capital investment. This method allows for the time value of money.

dominant trait—A dominating influence by one of a pair of allelic genes, when both are present in the germ plasm, to produce a dominant character.

dry matter—A substance, such as soil or feed, in relation to its moisture content and usually expressed in percent. For example, air-dry feed would be dried by natural air movement and would be approximately 85 to 90 percent dry matter, whereas moisture-free feed would be oven-dried and represent 100 percent dry matter.

dual-purpose breed—A breed of cattle that is used for both milk and meat production.

EBV—Estimated Breeding Value.

economy of gain—The daily rate of gain, as a result of feed consumed compared with the feed cost.

ear—In this book refers to cattle that have long droopy ears and believed to have Brahman blood or *Bos indicus* in their ancestry.

embryo transplantation—A process whereby a fertilized embryo is taken from a donor cow's oviduct and placed into the oviduct or uterus of a recipient cow.

EPA report—A report from the Environmental Protection Agency outlining the environmental status of a specific property.

EPD—Expected Progeny Difference.

estate in severalty—The ownership of property by only one person or legal entity.

estimated breeding value—The estimate of a genetic trait that is transmittable and reflects the animal's relatives's and progeny's performance data.

expected progeny difference—A technique and analysis that attempts to predict progeny performance such as birth weight, weaning weight, and other measurable traits.

F_1—The first cross or generation in a cattle breeding program.

feeder cattle—Cattle which are raised or bought, then fed solely for fattening and slaughter.

flood plain—An area, usually along a river, that is subject to periodic flooding.

forage—Herbaceous plants fed to domestic animals such as beef cattle.

future interest—A property right or estate that may not be enjoyed until some time in the future.

gene—Specific region of a chromosome that is capable of determining the development of a specific trait and consists primarily of DNA and protein.

gene pair—A pair of genes occupying the same relative position on homologous chromosomes that convey inherited characteristics.

genome mapping—The identification and mapping of a specific complement of haploid genes on a homologous chromosome.

gnomes—A group of imaginary beings that have occult or mysterious knowledge of the earth and its happenings.

gumbo-type soil—A fine silty soil that becomes sticky and nonporous when wet.

hardpan—A layer of hard soil, fastened together by a conglomeration of almost insoluble materials, that restricts the downward movement of water and roots.

heifer—A young female beef animal that has not borne a calf.

herd book—An official registry for recording the cattle of a particular breed.

heterozygous—An animal having two different genes at a single locus on a chromosome and hence not breeding true- to- type for a specific trait.

homestead—A house and contiguous land used as the primary place of residence for the head of a family.

Homestead Act—One of three laws designed to serve the interests of the family farmer enacted by the U.S. government in 1862. The law was modified through the years, but initially granted tracts of land to settlers for the development of farms. In addition, certain other provisions protect and support the farmer such as restrictions on creditors to seize and force sale of property for general obligation-type debt.

homozygous—An animal having two identical genes at a single locus on a chromosome and hence breeding true- to- type for a specific trait.

horizontal drilling—A technique for drilling oil and gas wells that provides for lateral movement of the drill bit, in addition to its normal vertical drilling pattern.

hybrid vigor—A phenomenon resulting from crossbreeding in which offspring exhibit greater vigor and resistance than their parents.

income tax basis—The original or other "cost" basis of the property, reduced by depreciation deductions and increased by capital expenditures.

installment contract—Also called a land contract. An installment-selling arrangement whereby the buyer may use, occupy and enjoy real property, but the deed is not given by the seller until all or a specified part of the sale price has been paid.

internal drainage—The process of removing the superfluous water from the soil profile, especially from its surface layer and upper subsoil.

internode—The part of a plant stem between two joints or nodes.

interparticle space—The space between soil particles and aggregates that contain air and water.

joint tenancy—Ownership of real property by two or more individuals, each of whom has an undivided interest with the right of survivorship as sole owner of the property upon the death of the other.

joint venture—An agreement between two or more parties who invest in a single property or business venture.

land contract— See: installment contract.

Land-Grant Act—A Federal act originally passed in 1862 and modified later designating each state or territory for federal aid in the form of land grants and subsequent financial support in order to establish separate institutions for instruction in agriculture and mechanical arts.

life interest—An interest in real estate for a period of the life of the one having the interest, or the life of another person described in the document that describes the life interest, such as a child of the person who has that life interest. Also called life estate.

limited partnership—A business organization consisting of one or more general partners who conduct the business and are liable for losses and one or more special or limited partners who contribute capital and are liable only up to the amount contributed.

loam—A rich soil. In technical terms, a soil classification based on texture, which consists of clay, sand and some organic matter in proportions usually considered to be the best for agricultural production.

Longhorn—A breed of long-horned cattle raised primarily in the South-west.

marbling—A pattern of streaked fat in the meat of an animal that is generally recognized as giving the beef "prime" quality flavor.

maternal traits—Traits associated with the mother's side of the family, such as milking ability and reproductive performance.

Mendel's laws—The four principles of heredity discovered and formulated by Gregor Mendel; i.e. the law of independent units or characters, the law of segregation, the law of dominance, and the law of independent assortment.

mill rate—A term used in expressing a tax rate, equal to one tenth of a cent.

mothering ability—A cowmen's term to describe the capability of a female animal to raise a calf, which refers mainly to the quantity of a cow's milk production.

nematode—A cylindrical, unsegmented, and translucent worm often parasitic on animals and plants.

nucleus—An oval mass of protoplasm, present in most animal and plant cells, containing most of the hereditary material necessary for growth and development.

offspring—A descendent or an animal related to its parent; progeny.

ova transfer—A mechanical transfer of a mature, fertilized germ cell from a donor cow to a recipient cow.

partnership—A business organization of two or more persons, organized to conduct, as co-owners, a business for profit. Partners are individually liable for the debts of the partnership and the income is divided and taxed as personal income to the individual partners.

permeability—A measure of the ease with which water can diffuse downward through the soil.

personal holding company—A corporation in which five or less shareholders own 50 percent or more of the outstanding stock and, generally, if 60 percent of its gross income is derived from dividends, interest, royalties, rental income or income from personal services performed by a substantial shareholder. Other criteria apply relating to the nature of the income earned by the corporation. A penalty tax may be imposed on undistributed personal holding company income. For American citizens, it is generally advised to avoid this classification and requires the attention of a qualified tax advisor.

pH—A symbol for the degree of acidity or alkalinity of a soil or solution; pH 7 is considered neutral, while pH values of 0 to 7 indicates acidity, and values of 7 to 14 are alkaline in nature.

pollarding—A pruning technique used in mature pecan groves whereby the trees are severely pruned and the top branches are cut back to the trunk.

polled—Cattle lacking horns; hornless.

purebred—Cattle belonging to a specific breed with characters maintained through generations. Not synonymous with registered cattle, as cattle may be purebred but not registered in the breed association's herd book.

rate of gain—A measure of the increase in weight of cattle per unit of time, such as the daily weight gain.

ration—The food supply for beef cattle.

recessive gene—One of any pair of allelic genes, when both are present in the germ plasm, that remains latent or a gene that is without appreciable effect when associated with its dominant allelomorph.

registered cattle—Cattle that meet the requirements and are recorded in the breed association's herd book.

replacement heifer—A young female animal that has calved, but is continued to be raised for inclusion in the breeding herd.

reproductive efficiency—A cowman's colloquial term, which usually means a characteristic of a cow that measures the total pounds of live beef at weaning, and incorporates such goals as having a calf each year and having it survive till weaning.

right of survivorship—In real estate refers to the right of a joint tenant (owner) to maintain ownership rights following the death of another joint tenant.

rosette—In plants, a condition where there is limited growth of the internodes of a terminal stem, creating a rosette appearance to the stem or twig. In pecans, usually a symptom of zinc deficiency.

roughage—A coarse fodder for beef cattle that has a relatively high proportion of fiber. In this book usually refers to pasture, hay or silage.

salts—A chemical compound derived from an acid by replacing the hydrogen portion of the molecule and in soils and water, usually consisting mainly of sodium, calcium, magnesium, chloride, and sulfate and secondarily of potassium, bicarbonate, carbonate, nitrate and boron.

sandy loam—A soil classification that is a combination of sand, silt, and clay particles in a proportion that offer suitable physical characteristics to a soil. A sandy loam soil will usually possess desirable qualities without exhibiting those undesirable properties such as low water holding capacity, stickiness, compactness, and slow water and gas movement. Usually considered a good agricultural soil.

Santa Cruz—A composite breed of beef cattle developed by the King Ranch in which the blood consists of one-half Santa Gertrudis, one-fourth Red Angus, and one-fourth Gelbieh.

seedstock—In the beef cattle industry, refers to purebred and/or registered cattle, either male or female, that can or should genetically improve efficiency of production and the quality of the end product.

scurred—Horny tissue of rudimentary horns that are attached to the skin rather than the skull bone.

silts—A soil classification whereby the soil particles have a high proportion of silt. Considered a fine-textured soil, or in layman's terms, heavy, because of the high water-holding capacity and difficult working qualities.

sire—The male parent of a beef animal.

Sire Summary—A compilation of registered sires and their performance records prepared and sponsored by their respective breed association.

small grain—In this book, a cool-season annual forage such as, wheat, oats or rye.

soil profile—A vertical-view of the soil down through the various layers to, or into, the parent material.

soil survey—A procedure with a resultant map that classifies, locates on a base map and describes soils as they appear in the field. In a soil conservation survey, land use, degree of erosion and slope are usually shown in addition to soil type.

soil type—A subdivision in a soil classification system that is based on the texture of the top soil and designated as loam, sandy loam, and so on.

static level—As used in this book, refers to the dynamic underground water level in a well after it has been pumped for a significant period of time at the usual discharge rate.

steer—A castrated male calf that is raised and fed for slaughter.

stocker—A young beef animal after weaning, raised as a replacement heifer in a breeding herd, or to be put into the feedlot for finishing or fattening.

subchapter S—A section of the Internal Revenue Code that governs S Corporations or those with a limited number of shareholders, electing to be taxed as a partnership, but legally conducting business as a corporation with limited legal liability.

switch—The bushy, or end, portion of the tail on a beef animal.

tank—A colloquial term for farm pond.

tenancy in common—A legal term meaning the undivided ownership of property by two or more persons, but without the right of survivorship.

tenancy in the entireties—A form of ownership by a husband and wife whereby each owns the entire property, but in the event of death of one, the survivor owns the property without probate.

time is of the essence—A phrase that may be inserted into a contract to bind one party to performance at or by a specified time in order to bind the other party to timely performance.

topline—The top portion of the back, generally between the shoulders and the last rib on a beef animal. In financial parlance refers to the revenue line of an income and expense statement.

topographic map—A map that shows the surface features, such as elevations and depths, roads, ponds, and streams of a particular piece of land.

topography—The science of depicting the surface features of land including elevations, depths, rivers, lakes, and man-made features such as roads, canals, and bridges.

Triple Crown—In horse racing, refers to winning the Kentucky Derby, the Preakness and the Belmont Stakes in the same year.

ultrasound—A technology that utilizes ultrasonic waves for diagnostic and analytical purposes. In the beef industry used to determine back fat, loin eye area and pregnancy testing.

underline—The belly area in beef cattle.

undivided interest—A partial interest by two or more persons in the same property regardless of whether the interests are equal. No co-owner has exclusive rights to any portion of the property.

water-holding capacity—A semi-technical term to describe the capacity of the soil to retain water after an adequate opportunity for drainage. Soils of heavy texture and high colloidal content such as most clays have a high water-holding capacity, while sandy soils at the other end of the spectrum usually have a low capacity.

water rights—The legal right to use water from an underground aquifer, stream, river, and canal.

weaning weight—The actual weight of a calf at the time of weaning or separation from its mother and usually adjusted to 205 days.

Zebu types—A species of beef cattle native to Asia and parts of Africa that has a prominent hump over its shoulders, pendulous ears, and considered more resistant to heat and insect-borne diseases.

Index

Country Properties

About the Authors

John and Jennifer Hoff are a father/daughter team who have grown their agribusiness and real estate business together and now have produced this book to help the scores of people interested in buying rural real estate. Both have been formally educated in the subject matter and have spent essentially their entire business careers in marketing, financing, and managing agricultural businesses and real estate.

John K. Hoff earned his B.S. from Rutgers University and Ph.D. from Cornell University in the agricultural sciences. Immediately thereafter he entered the commercial sector of the global agricultural industry, first, in marketing, then in financial management, and ultimately as president and chief executive officer of an internationally known agribusiness firm. He also served on the boards of several companies in the Middle East and Latin America as well as the board and investment committee of the Boyce Thompson Institute for Plant Research, and the board and executive committee of the Agribusiness Council of New York. Dr. Hoff, with a keen interest in education, was an active chairman of several Cornell University committees, a moderator, "Being the Best Overseas," First Entrepreneur of the Year Symposium, Johnson Graduate School of Management, Cornell University and served three terms on the Cornell Council. Additionally, he has been agribusiness advisor to several national governments and served on the organizing or executive committees of agricultural investment missions to eighteen countries. He was on the board of a major national bank, served as trustee for several major families, including a King Ranch family member and taught marketing management at the University of Houston for two semesters. Importantly, he has been the owner of several prominent farms and ranches, a purebred beef cattle herd and several world-class hunting and jumping horses. Currently, he is chairman of The Seville Group and lives in Texas with his family.

Jennifer L. Hoff is an experienced real estate advertising and marketing executive. A native Texan, she received a B.S. from Cornell University specializing in agricultural economics, marketing and real estate. During the ten years since graduation from college, Jennifer has worked in the real estate brokerage business, both in marketing and advertising/public affairs, then as personal assistant to the well-known and admired former editor-in-chief of *National Geographic* magazine, Bill Garrett, and finally as president and chief operating officer of The Seville Group. She has represented several of the world's highest net-worth individuals and both domestic and international companies in their real estate investments and transactions. Jennifer lives in Texas with her two Korat cats, Ling Ling and Oliver.

An aerial photograph such as the one on the opposite page can be very helpful in studying the geography of the land, the surface drainage, field layout, location of roads, improvements and boundaries as well as the type and extent of vegetation, such as permanent pasture or cultivatable land. The aerial photograph is commonly used in conjunction with a soil map, thereby providing a means for systematically evaluating the entire farm or ranch.

Aerial photographs can usually be obtained from the USDA Farm Service Agency in the county where the land is located. There may also be local commercial aerial photographers who have more recent photographs.